LIFE NATURE LIBRARY

THE
POLES

OTHER BOOKS BY THE EDITORS OF LIFE:

LIFE NATURE LIBRARY

THE
POLES

by Willy Ley
and The Editors of LIFE

TIME INCORPORATED
NEW YORK

A STONEHENGE BOOK

About the Author

Willy Ley is a writer and lecturer in many fields of science. He has been absorbed by the natural sciences, particularly zoology and geology, since his student days, and has long been fascinated with the polar regions as remnants of the ice ages. Born in Berlin on October 2, 1906, Ley attended the Universities of Berlin and Königsberg. He came to the U.S. in 1935, served as science editor of the New York newspaper *PM* from 1940 to 1944 and as a research engineer at the Washington Institute of Technology from 1944 to 1947. His books include: *Willy Ley's Exotic Zoology; Engineers' Dreams; The Lands Beyond* (with L. S. de Camp); *Rockets, Missiles and Space Travel; The Conquest of Space;* and *The Exploration of Mars* (with Wernher von Braun). He belongs to the American Association for the Advancement of Science, the Institute of Aerospace Sciences, the American Rocket Society, the Society of Military Engineers and Canada's Royal Astronomical Society.

ON THE COVER: Pack ice, jumbled by the immense forces of tide and wind, covers the sea off the coast of Antarctica. The glittering scene was photographed near the U.S. station at McMurdo Sound.

Contents

TIME INC. BOOK DIVISION

Editor: NORMAN P. ROSS

Copy Director: WILLIAM JAY GOLD   *Art Director:* EDWARD A. HAMILTON

Chief of Research: BEATRICE T. DOBIE

•

EDITORIAL STAFF FOR "THE POLES":

Editor, LIFE Nature Library: MAITLAND EDEY

Assistant to the Editor: GEORGE McCUE

Copy Editor: RICHARD L. WILLIAMS

Copy Associate: CARL SOLBERG

Designer: PAUL JENSEN

Chief Researcher: MARTHA TURNER

Researchers: JOAN ALLEN, DORIS BRY, PEGGY BUSHONG,
ELEANOR FELTSER, LE CLAIR G. LAMBERT, PAULA NORWORTH,
SHEILA OSMUNDSEN, ROXANNA SAYRE, VICTOR H. WALDROP,
PHYLLIS M. WILLIAMSON

Picture Researchers: MARGARET K. GOLDSMITH, SUE E. THALBERG

Art Associate: ROBERT L. YOUNG

Art Assistants: JAMES D. SMITH, MARK A. BINN

Copy Staff: MARIAN GORDON GOLDMAN, SUZANNE SEIXAS, DOLORES A. LITTLES

•

Publisher: JEROME S. HARDY

General Manager: JOHN A. WATTERS

•

LIFE MAGAZINE

Editor
EDWARD K. THOMPSON

Managing Editor
GEORGE P. HUNT

Publisher
C. D. JACKSON

•

The text for the chapters of this book was written by Willy Ley, for the picture essays by Gerald Simons, David Thomson and Hubert Kay. The following individuals and departments of LIFE Magazine were helpful in producing the book: Fritz Goro and George Silk, staff photographers; Thomas N. Carmichael, Chief of Regional Editors; and Doris O'Neil, Chief of the LIFE Picture Library. Assistance was also given by Donald Bermingham of the TIME-LIFE News Service, and Content Peckham, Chief of the Time Inc. Bureau of Editorial Reference.

Introduction

ONE attribute makes the earth unique among all the satellites of the sun—the abundance of the molecule H_2O in its three forms of water, water vapor and ice. Without these commonplace substances we could not exist, yet it is only by accidents of gravity and temperature that we have them. If our planet were appreciably smaller, and thus had weaker gravity, most of the water would have evaporated into space long ago (this is probably what has happened to our dry neighbor, Mars). The temperature range of our air is only one among an infinite number of possibilities, yet it luckily encompasses the relatively few degrees in which water, ice and water vapor can coexist.

Even more delicate is the temperature balance between water and ice. Time and time again the balance has shifted to favor the ice, and glaciers have advanced to cover most of the earth we know, then retreated for long periods when even Greenland and Antarctica were places of warm forests and plains. Why this balance shifts, we do not begin to understand.

Today we are entering an era of unlimited power, when science may be able to alter the temperature balance and convert the cold regions to hospitable, productive ones. To do this would require the greatest political courage, for the rewards certainly would not be equally divided over all political borders. But if it were done, the problem of containing and feeding future generations could be solved. Unfortunately we as a nation are not yet confronted with the problem and we give it only token attention; but world storms generated by hunger are brewing.

All this considers only one of the facets of the polar regions. Here also are concentrated the intricacies of the upper atmosphere—the pulsations of the ionosphere, the flickering auroras, the sweeping magnetic storms. These center above the magnetic poles, and they must be studied—for who can foresee the benefits to mankind that may come from the solution of all these polar mysteries?

The polar scientist has many problems. His work is by nature uncomfortable and inefficient, and he works hard and long for scattered bits of data. He rarely is left alone to experiment, but too often is steered in the directions dictated by funds and facilities. Eventually these must be his to use as he desires if the work in these areas is to remain attractive to those who can best contribute.

This book fascinatingly describes and wonderfully illustrates the polar regions as they are now and as they have been. Indeed, the beauties of the land make us wonder if they were not meant to be left so, but history teaches otherwise, and the growth of mankind has no limits.

ALBERT P. CRARY
Chief Scientist
Office of Antarctic Programs
National Science Foundation

1

The Cold, Far Frontiers

AMONG the provinces of our planet the polar regions are unique. They are in every sense the extremes of the earth. They are the domain of cold, which is the antithesis of life. The Greenland and antarctic icecaps are the only absolute deserts, the only utterly lifeless places. Yet for the globe at large, these enormous reservoirs of cold are a world-wide influence—even though the people who live far from them do not realize it—for they send out their storms and their tempering chill everywhere and so shape the habitat that has nourished all life and every civilization.

The poles have long been a challenge, remote and forbidding, to man's sense of venture and curiosity. Today, in the sweep of technological revolution, the Arctic has become a highway, and tomorrow both the polar regions may be exploited for food, minerals and other materials needed to support man's steadily expanding population. Already nine out of every 10 human beings live on the continents bordering the North Polar Basin, and the most powerful nations of the earth now form a ring around the North Pole. The geography of history has shifted since man has taken to the air, and today the North Polar Basin has become the new Mediterranean,

9

"the Middle Sea" of the earth. Aircraft traverse it in flying the shortest route, the great circle, between two continents. The projected track of intercontinental rockets leads right over it. For better or worse, the Arctic is central to the 20th Century world.

There is some dispute about how to define these polar regions, especially in the case of the Arctic. The expert who sees things in botanical terms will bound the Arctic by the northern limit of trees. The climate specialist will draw his border along the widely shifting line that marks a 50° average temperature for the warmest month. The geologist tends to fix polar boundaries by continental limits—adequate for the Antarctic but not so helpful for the Arctic, for its most notable feature is a small ocean surrounded by continents extending far to the south. These definitions suit particular, not general, scientific viewpoints and are based on factors that keep changing. Worse, they tend to define a condition rather than a place.

There is another kind of polar boundary to which none of these criticisms applies—a natural boundary that is as fixed as the stars in their courses and just as little subject to influence by changing climate, vegetation or terrain. That permanent boundary for both polar regions is light. Because of the tilted axis of the earth each geographical pole is in turn tilted 23½° from a plane vertical to the earth's orbit around the sun. The 23½° lines are marked upon globes as the Arctic and Antarctic Circles, 66½° north and south latitude respectively. The relation of these two astronomically determined boundaries to the lighting of the poles is as follows: upon each circle for one 24-hour day in winter the sun never rises, and conversely for one 24-hour day in summer the sun never sets. Poleward from each circle the winter darkness increases and the summer light increases, until at the poles themselves there is but one day in a whole year —six months' continuous light and six months' continuous darkness. The dividing times for this prodigiously long polar day are the vernal and autumnal equinoxes, when the duration of light and dark is equal over the entire globe.

IN a sense the poles are abstractions: the ancient Greeks were able to imagine both north and south poles at the ends of the earth 3,000 years before Peary and Amundsen found them. But the poles are real places, no doubt about that, and very different places too. One way to describe their relationship to each other is to say that the Arctic is a hollow in the top of the globe, and the Antarctic a corresponding bulge on the bottom. It is almost as if an immense dent, caused by the pressure of some cosmic thumb, had been made at the North Pole, its effect passing all through the earth to emerge as a swelling at the South Pole. The dent in the top of the world is the Arctic Ocean, the world's smallest; the corresponding

THE MIDNIGHT SUN is a phenomenon (right) explained by the inclination of the earth on its axis as it travels its elliptical orbit around the sun.

● In June, at the summer solstice, the earth stands in the left-hand position in the diagram. For one day the earth is so placed that as it revolves, the entire Arctic receives 24 hours of sunlight. During this same day, the Antarctic is in continual darkness.

● In December, at the winter solstice, the earth stands in the right-hand position in the diagram. When it is so located, the entire Antarctic receives 24 hours of sun and the Arctic lies in darkness.

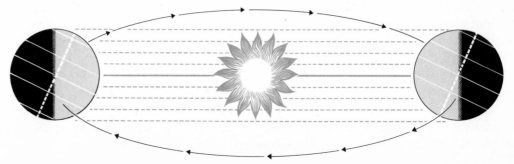

bulge at the bottom of the globe is the continent of Antarctica. Such a view of these true antipodes reveals the remarkable exactitude of the contrast between them. In size they are nearly the same, the Arctic Ocean being 5,541,000 square miles in area, the antarctic continent 5,100,000 square miles. The average depth of the Arctic Ocean, 4,200 feet, is approximated by Antarctica's mean elevation of 6,000 feet, which makes it the highest of all the continents. Even the greatest depth of the Arctic Ocean, 17,500 feet, has its antipode in Antarctica's highest mountain, Mount Fridtjof Nansen, which rises to 19,000 feet above sea level. Most startling of all is a likeness in shape so marked that one polar region might almost be superimposed upon the other, the Arctic Ocean's one deep outlet down the east coast of Greenland matching the southern continent's sole outthrust arm in the Palmer Peninsula.

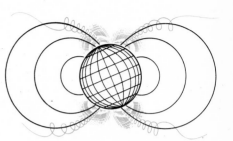

THE AURORAS appear as shadings in the diagram above. The earth's strong magnetic field arcs out from the North and South Magnetic Poles. Atomic particles emitted by the sun are trapped in this field and spiral toward the poles along the lines of magnetic force, causing the gases in the polar atmosphere to glow.

THE Arctic and Antarctic, then, are proverbial opposites—"poles apart," as we say. But before looking at their differences let us note what they have in common. Both have a net loss of heat from the sun, for instance (whereas the tropics have a net gain). In their present state of cold, foul weather, both the north and south icecaps are remnants of an ice age that descended upon the globe only a million years ago. For most of the billions of years before that, they shared the warm and equable climate that usually has prevailed over the earth in general.

The polar regions are also alike in producing certain oddities of light. This is true quite apart from the eerie noon darkness and bright midnight that result from the way the earth is tilted. The Arctic and Antarctic are forever amazing and confounding the traveler from lower latitudes with fantastic mirages caused by the bending of low-slanting sunlight as it passes through layers of cold air. The polar skies also abound with sundogs, or parhelia, double and triple mock moons, and other bizarre sky phenomena rarely seen elsewhere. Above all, the polar skies are the classic stage for the glittering theatrical displays put on by the northern and southern lights, aurora borealis and aurora australis.

Polar auroras appear in gorgeously colored arcs, rays, bands, patches and—most often—as waving curtains in the dark heavens. Although the lore of all northern peoples is rich with more fanciful explanations, we now know that an aurora is caused by charged particles from the sun striking rarefied gases of the ionosphere and illuminating them. In other words, the lights are made by electrical storms 50 to 600 miles up, in much the same way that neon light is made in a tube. Perhaps the unearthliest thing about this "high lightning" is the total absence of any sound accompanying it.

Of all the differences between the arctic and antarctic regions, the biggest is that the Antarctic has so much more ice—probably eight times as much. This is because the Antarctic is a continent, a poor heat conserver, whereas the Arctic is primarily an ocean, which has a superior capacity for storing summer heat and moderating the cold of winter. All but the barest edge of the entire antarctic continent is still covered by an ice sheet with an average thickness of more than a mile. In the Arctic, the last great ice sheets of the ice age never covered the North Pole at all but spread from various centers hundreds of miles to the south; all that is left of them today are the icecaps of Greenland and the rest of the high Arctic.

IN its heartland the Antarctic is a vast dome of ice formed by the snows of ages past. Even more than the Arctic it is essentially a desert area, receiving little moisture in the course of the year. Near the 13,000-foot top of this dome, at the so-called "pole of inaccessibility" (over 400 miles from the South Pole itself), it is so high and so cold that the air simply cannot hold much water vapor, and snowfall is light. Over the continent as a whole, perhaps five inches of precipitation falls annually in the form of snow. However, this meager fall lasts because of the extreme low temperatures. The white surface reflects back into space up to 90 per cent of the sun's heat, which is less intense at the poles than at any other point on earth because it strikes at an oblique angle. On the surface the snow slowly turns into tiny granules of ice. These become denser under pressure, melting near the surface and refreezing lower down, growing larger and larger until at 60 to 100 feet down the individual grains attain an average diameter of two inches. Out of such building blocks, laid down over a million or more years, the glacier takes its mighty form.

The mechanism of glaciers requires that to grow or at least hold their own, they receive as much snow each year as they lose by melting and evaporation. Apparently, most of the world's glaciers today are not maintaining a balance on the side of accumulation, and there are many examples, like those of Lingen Fjord in northern Norway, which within the memory of living men flowed into the sea but have now retreated far up their valleys. But scientists are by no means sure that the antarctic ice sheet, biggest of all glaciers, is shrinking. Its weight, pressing down upon the earth's plastic crust, depresses the land below sea level in many areas, a phenomenon that caused some scientists to ask for a time whether Antarctica might really be a series of large islands and not a continent at all.

THE TOP OF THE WORLD, as it would appear from a vantage point high over Canada's Northwest Territories, is an ocean ringed by land. North of the permafrost line the land areas are permanently frozen. North of the tree line lies the tundra. The limit of each map on these pages is 50° north or south latitude.

Seismic ice soundings carried out during and after the 1957-1958 International Geophysical Year confirmed that Antarctica is indeed a continent. But most of the great area called Marie Byrd Land turned out to be so far below sea level that even if all the weight of the ice should be removed it probably would not rise above the water. Accordingly, cartographers now can draw a large bay where much of Marie Byrd Land appears to be.

Receding or not, the antarctic ice sheet is definitely on the move. All ice tends to flow and find its own level just as water does, but much more slowly. A flake of snow falling at the South Pole can take thousands of years to find its way to the ocean, but it does get there. The icecap slides against the coastal mountains, then rides up over them in a "plastic flow" that can move some parts of the ice as much as 2,500 feet a year.

This outward flow to the sea has produced a phenomenon peculiar to the Antarctic, the so-called barrier ice. Having crunched down to the sea, great, raftlike masses of ice push across the buried coast line and right out to the open ocean, still maintaining their glacial form. In the Ross Sea this barrier and the solid ice shelf behind it extend as much as 500 miles out from land over a 400-mile front—an area as large as France. Where it meets the open sea and finally breaks off in huge iceberg fragments, the barrier presents a face of sheer ice cliffs 150 feet high. The fragments that break off are the characteristic "tabular" flat-topped icebergs of the Antarctic. They are not nearly so picturesque as the grotesquely sculptured bergs that drift south from Greenland but they are infinitely larger, often 50 miles long and 1,000 feet thick.

Just as continental Antarctica is the abode of the ice sheet, the oceanic Arctic is the world's great freezer for sea ice. When the temperature of salt water falls to about 28°, sea ice begins to form. In an arctic winter,

THE BOTTOM OF THE WORLD, as it would appear from a vantage point above the mid-south Pacific Ocean, is a land mass ringed by oceans. The small squares indicate locations of International Geophysical Year scientific bases. On both maps, areas of drift ice are shown in medium blue, and areas of pack ice in pale blue.

ice forms over most of the North Polar Basin, covering an expanse 1,900 to 2,500 miles and several feet thick. This is pack ice, and many of its floes remain for years, melting partly in summer, growing again in the following winter, sometimes reaching a thickness of 13 feet before being carried south by currents. Occasionally giant sheets of pack ice, always in motion and drifting with the wind or currents, collide. Where they slam together pressure ridges form as one sheet slides on top of another. Often, after many seasons' grinding and splitting, the surface of pack ice becomes rubble. In the spring the pack ice begins to melt, fresh-water lakes spread across its surface and great "leads" open up between the floes.

THE Antarctic too has its pack ice which in winter fills the bays and gulfs to seaward for hundreds of miles and is just as capable of crushing a ship as arctic pack ice—as Ernest Shackleton found when his *Endurance* became frozen in the Weddell Sea ice in 1915. Navigating through ice is a bit easier in the Antarctic than in the Arctic, however, because the prevailing southeasterly winds blow the ice offshore and during the brief four-to-eight-week summer there is likely to be open water near the land if a ship can just break through to it.

Antarctic wind—like all antarctic weather—is in a class by itself. The winds whirl off the immense south polar ice dome with a ferocity seldom matched on earth. Raging across the antarctic latitudes—the "Shrieking 60s"—they bump into the prevailing westerlies that blow around the world just south of Cape Horn and Australia, and either sweep back over the pole or send storms blasting into the South Atlantic, Pacific and Indian Oceans. This circulation of cold antarctic air, incidentally, is more than matched by the circulation of slow-creeping "Antarctic Bottom Water," which cools all the oceans and helps regulate the whole world's climate.

The antarctic continent, says Frank Debenham, one of the Scott expedition's geologists, is "the home of the wind." Air, chilled and thereby made heavy, is forever flowing down off the high plateau. Along the mountain dikes that rim part of the continent, winds drive snow seaward in long blizzards that cut visibility to less than three feet. Sometimes gusts have been known to reach 200 miles an hour. The worst of antarctic wind is that it hardly ever lets up.

At the very center of the continent the air is relatively calm—and cold. At the United States South Pole Station the temperature often drops to 100° below zero. The lowest reading on the globe was made August 24, 1960, at the Soviet plateau station of Vostok, which is 2,300 feet higher than the pole: -126.9°. Nearer the coast it never gets that cold, but the return of the sun in summer, while it melts snow in the neighborhood of rocks and thaws out a few shallow ponds, is negligible as a heat source. There is no month in the year when the mean temperature anywhere in the Antarctic goes above freezing.

The Arctic is much milder and much less hostile to life. It is cold enough in winter: temperatures of 60° below are common in many places. But at the very polar caps, where Antarctica is frozen solid, the Arctic has the moderating presence of the sea just under the ice pack. As a result the northern "cold pole" is nowhere near the geographical pole: it is some 1,500 miles to the south, just within the Arctic Circle at Verkhoyansk in eastern Siberia. There the temperature has touched 90° below.

But in summer the temperature at Verkhoyansk averages 60° above, and it is this brief warm-up phase of the arctic climate that gives life the chance it never gets in the Antarctic. Arctic summers, especially at such inland places, can be extremely hot, and the thermometer can stay up for a month or more. This summer heat, and the moisture it releases during thaw, make possible a surprisingly abundant vegetation. Besides many mosses, lichens and algae, there are hundreds of kinds of flowering plants. These thrive even on Peary Land, the northernmost land in the world.

From the air much of the north polar region appears as a world in creation. Where the great ice sheet has melted, it has left a land strewn with boulders and laced with so many streams, bogs and lakes that the surface often seems more water than dry land. Into this region vegetation is gradually encroaching, and the process of creating new soil is everywhere evident. The ponds and oxbows of former rivers fill with water plants, then marsh grasses take root in a tightening circle, and these in turn give a foothold to land plants. Given the right conditions, these marsh and land plants keep on using up water until the pond shrinks to a small central circle and finally disappears, leaving a patch of dry ground fertilized by decaying vegetation.

Normally this process would result in the steady manufacture of soils, but arctic conditions are not normal. It takes a long time to get over an ice age. A lack of bacteria in earth and air slows the soil-building: in many areas peat bogs have been built up, too acid to support more than a few types of plants. Most arctic land, moreover, consists of permanently frozen ground, or permafrost, extending as much as 1,600 feet down. Permafrost is shallowest near the seacoasts, deepest in the big inland stretches which get the coldest weather.

During the summer the top few inches above this permafrost thaw out, and it is in this moist top layer that plants form their roots and sprout. Slim as this margin for life is, it is eagerly seized during the brief arctic summer when the tiny flowering plants spread their brave carpet of color. But the permafrost just beneath the surface makes the whole face of the arctic earth unstable and shifty. All along the bleak northern border where trees verge into tundra, trees can put down only shallow roots. They grow up at a tilt, leaning now one way, now another. Scientists call this curious spectacle "the drunken forest."

THE final contrast between the arctic and antarctic regions is to be seen in the different appearance and structure of their land masses. Throughout the mostly flat and open Arctic there is abundant evidence of its far different past. On West Spitsbergen, for example, there are numerous fjords whose cliff walls are horizontally banded for hundreds of miles by layered sediments. These sediments bear fossils of warm-sea animals, leaves and trunks from warm-temperate forests, petrified logs and needles from giant *Metasequoia* trees. Such evidence may be found in many other areas, such as Greenland, Baffin Island, Alaska and even in Antarctica.

Many of these ocean-bottom sediments have been pushed several hundred feet above the present sea level by the elevation of the land, or by the withdrawal of water from the seas. In some places former beaches run far up into the land in sharp steps, and in others the imbedded bones of modern sea mammals are found in high altitudes, miles from water.

Much of Antarctica, however, is spiny and mountainous, with steep shores and no exposed coastal plain worth the name. A few isolated valleys are bare, their rocky sides wind-swept; and here and there a small pocket enclosing a pond appears as a small oasis in the vast white waste. Several mountain ranges thrust through the icecap, notably the Queen Maud Range, which bisects the continent much as the submerged Lomonosov Ridge divides the Arctic Ocean. One of the most picturesque monuments on the continent is 13,000-foot Mount Erebus, the continent's only live volcano, looming above the main United States base at McMurdo Sound.

The corner of Antarctica with the most exposed surface is the jagged Palmer Peninsula, which juts out over 200 miles beyond the Antarctic Circle to a latitude comparable with that of central Norway. At its tip the peninsula is only 600 miles below the southernmost point of the American continent. Though more vegetation is found here than anywhere else in Antarctica, it does not amount to much. There are just two flowering plants. And among its lichens and mosses live the continent's greatest variety of land animals—a few mites in the vicinity of penguin rookeries, ticks, wingless springtails and lice, and flies. Even these must be able to exist through most of the year in a frozen state and then thaw out for a brief burst of life and procreation under the direct rays of the sun. And not every year has a thaw.

Yet fossil leaves discovered in coal on inland mountain slopes by the Scott expedition 50 years ago suggest that a luxuriant life once flourished in Antarctica, and scientists have since turned up other geologic evidence that the continent, like the Arctic, once was warm.

THEN how did the polar regions get so cold? As might be expected, there are countless theories. Dr. Paul Siple, first leader of the IGY South Pole station, believes that the earth, like some unsteady gyroscope, has slowly wobbled on its axis, causing the location of the poles to shift. Two Lamont Geological Observatory scientists, Maurice Ewing and William L. Donn, do not believe the poles have migrated, or that the earth ever flipped on its axis. Their idea is that the earth's entire crust has slowly slid around the core, so that the Pacific and Indian Oceans, once located at the polar regions, traveled to their present positions while the Arctic Ocean and Antarctica shifted from temperate regions to the poles. According to an earlier theory, the continents have drifted like floating islands on the earth's plastic mantle, and at various times one or another has floated over the poles.

Other scientists have traced the onset of polar cold to world-wide volcanic eruptions spouting dust and gases into the atmosphere and so cutting off heat from the sun. Another hypothesis blames the big chill on a burst of mountain-building, which caused a critical loss of heat into space. The successive retreats of the ice-age glaciers are then ascribed to variations in heat output from the sun—the "Sunspot" theory.

All these theories have merit, and offer incidental understanding of many curious problems. Perhaps one, or a combination, in time will explain the phenomenon that has provided life with its sternest tests on earth. As yet no theory is wholly satisfying. The Arctic and Antarctic remain mysterious, their beginnings not understood. But as influences on every human environment, they are a major challenge for investigation.

THE ARCTIC'S HARSH LOOK SOFTENS IN SPRING: THAWING PACK ICE LITTERS CHUKCHI SEA OFF ALASKA LATE ON AN APRIL NIGHT

The Ends of the Earth

The silent immensities around the poles are the most unearth-
ly looking places on earth. Here the accustomed rhythms of
night and day are upset; strange lights disturb the sky, and
vistas that are most beautiful to the eye are chilling to the soul.
Man has penetrated these frigid fortresses, even lived in them,
but cannot yet boast that he has truly "conquered" the poles.

THE NORTH POLE lies somewhere below the wing tip of a commercial jet en route from Copenhagen to Tokyo, amid drifting ice floes stitched with pressure ridges and splashed with pools of melt-water.

The North and South Poles

In spite of superficial similarities visible in the pictures at the right, the North and South Poles are radically different. The geographic location of the North Pole is as difficult to pinpoint as it is to reach. It lies amid a clashing, grinding jumble of pack ice which drifts haltingly clockwise, round and round in the Arctic Ocean. Since an ice formation that identifies the pole one week may float a mile away the next, the only means of locating the pole exactly is by instruments.

By comparison, the South Pole is situated on solid land—more precisely, on 9,200 feet of glacial ice which in turn lies on the base rock of the antarctic continent. At the pole this rock has been pressed down to sea level by the sheer weight of the ice sheet, which contains more than 90 per cent of the world's ice. Due largely to its altitude, the South Pole has by far the more severe climate. Temperatures 140° below freezing —some 50° lower than the North Pole's lowest— have been registered at or near the South Pole. And midsummer, which may boost temperatures above freezing at the North Pole, rarely raises those at the South Pole above zero. There the extreme cold also makes the winds seem more savage. They blow at velocities averaging 15 miles an hour throughout the year, and gusts have reached 55 miles an hour during blizzards.

THE SOUTH POLE lies near a busy U.S. scientific station, atop nearly two miles of ice. It is 500 feet below the airstrip cleared in the snow, at a point two inches to the left of the center of the picture.

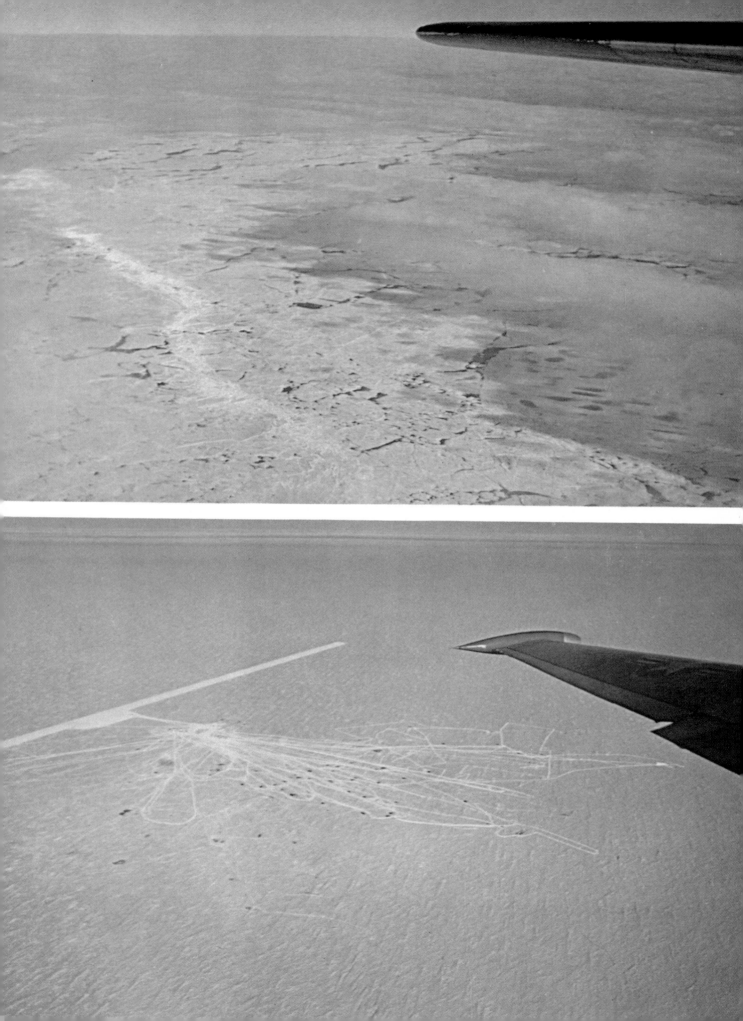

Days without End

The midnight sun does not set in this picture sequence, taken one June day on a Norwegian island well above the Arctic Circle. In exposures made at hourly intervals, the sun appears to climb and dip, reaching its zenith in the south at 11:27 a.m. and its lowest point in the north at 11:27 p.m.

Actually the earth's rotation on its tilted axis creates the illusion. Because of this tilt, 23.5° off the perpendicular, the earth in its annual orbit inclines one pole toward the sun for six months, the other for the rest of the year. Six months after the pictures were taken, this panorama had faded from nightless day to dayless night and the sun was at its height in the far south.

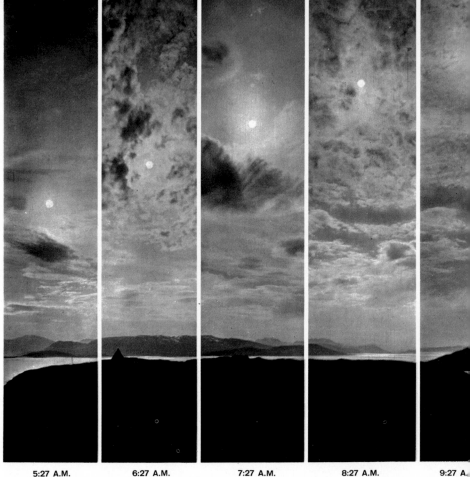

5:27 A.M.   6:27 A.M.   7:27 A.M.   8:27 A.M.   9:27 A.

4:27 P.M.   5:27 P.M.   6:27 P.M.   7:27 P.M.   8:27 P.M.   9:27 P.M.

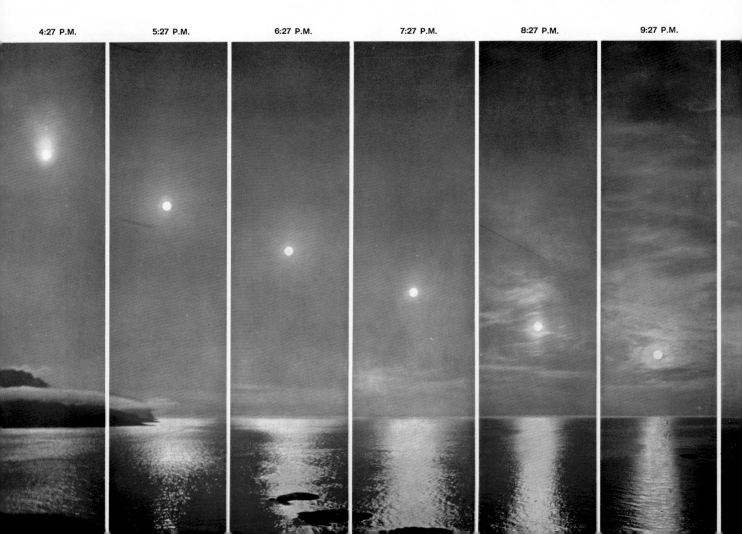

10:27 A.M.   11:27 A.M.   12:27 P.M.   1:27 P.M.   2:27 P.M.   3:27 P.M.

10:27 P.M.   11:27 P.M.   12:27 A.M.   1:27 A.M.   2:27 A.M.   3:27 A.M.   4:27 A.M.

A GREEN-RAYED AURORA sends spraylike arcs flickering aloft from horizon to zenith in Alaska. Like the glare of a neon tube, auroral light is caused by rarefied gases glowing under the impact of electrically charged particles. Displays of particular brilliance occur at 11-year intervals, in conjunction with great gaseous flare-ups on the sun's surface.

SHEETS OF RED LIGHT SUFFUSE THE ALASKAN SKY. THIS AURORA WAS SO BRIGHT IT WAS SEEN AS FAR SOUTH AS MEXICO CITY

The Auroral Spectacles

On certain nights, mostly in the spring and fall, ghostly veils and streamers of varicolored light shimmer in the sky far to the north and south. These awesome auroras are caused by atomic particles, protons and electrons, which are ejected in an unsteady stream from the sun. As the solar particles enter the earth's magnetic field and are pulled toward either geomagnetic pole, they collide with particles of nitrogen and oxygen in the atmosphere, causing them to glow. The color of an aurora's light depends on the altitudes at which these collisions occur and on the wave lengths of the particles involved. The highest collisions—as far as 600 miles up—usually create luminous sheets of blue; but on rare occasions, glows of red appear (*above*). From 50 to 175 miles up, yellowish coronas are produced by a mixture of high red auroras with low green ones. At these lower levels, many auroras take elaborate waterfall or arc shapes, like the one opposite.

23

MILKY CLIFFS, reaching some 150 feet above and 850 feet below the water, loom at the edge of the Ross Ice Shelf, which extends from Antarctica's continental ice sheet in a seagoing plain almost as large as France. Like water, though at speeds a million times slower, the ice sheet seeks a lower level, flowing out and down from its vast domed core in the

continent's interior. Reaching the coast, the ice pushes forward, often grinding on the irregular sea bottom until, in deeper water, it is a floating shelf. Along its 400-mile front, pieces start cracking in the rise and fall of the tide. They break loose, or "calve," as huge icebergs, some 100 miles long. These tend to be flat, whereas arctic bergs are jagged.

Plants under Siege

No plants at all grow in the sterile reaches of the Arctic and Antarctic which are permanently iced over. Even bacteria, which flourish by the millions in every spoonful of the poorest tropical soil, are all but absent here: one study at the South Pole counted only one per pint of snow.

But where the ice has retreated to reveal the naked land, plants have taken a firm foothold. The Antarctic's ice-free surface is largely confined to the narrow, rocky, wind-swept edges of the continental ice sheet. Here most plant life takes primitive forms like lichens and mosses, whose simple bodies are tolerant of great extremes of cold and dryness. Some 400 lichens and 75 kinds of mosses have been identified, but in all of Antarctica there are only two flowering plants, one a variety of grass and the other a relative of the carnation. The tremendous ice-free areas of the north are far more heavily vegetated. The arctic flora includes about 900 kinds of hardy flowers as well as 2,000 species of lichens and 500 of lushly growing mosses (*left*).

A SOGGY CARPET of brilliant mosses (*left*) comes to life in the blue water of melting snow as spring rolls north in central Canada. At lower left are sprigs of arctic grass.

A SERE RIBBON of struggling plants traces a brook of meltwater in Canada's Arctic (*below*). The soil is so unstable on steep slopes that most rooting plants cannot take hold.

Illusions in the Polar Air

At times the polar regions are transformed into a realm of fantasy, where the senses are befuddled by the strange actions of cold air and by drastic temperature extremes. Light rays may bounce between the ice and low clouds, creating a blinding opalescence called "white-out," which wipes out every landmark. "Snow down," fluffy balls of crystalline ice, may appear in air that warms faster than the snow below it. Mock moons, wheels of light and sundogs (*below*) are conjured by millions of ice-crystal prisms in the sky.

Mirages (*opposite*) appear in more varied shapes in arctic cold than in desert heat. In an illusion known to explorers as "looming," two layers of air of contrasting density—a cool and denser one under a warm one—act as a lens to bend light rays. This brings a distant, low-lying object into focus and makes it appear close at hand. At times the bent rays cause dual images to appear, the lower one turned upside down. Even the sun, near the end of its winter absence, may appear in a mirage several days before it really rises.

SUNDOGS are bright spots of light at opposite sides of a "halo," or ring around the sun. The halo itself is created by the bending of the sun's rays as they pass through air filled with ice crystals. At a point on each side of the sun the crystals act as tiny mirrors, reflecting the sun and forming the brilliant sundog highlights on the halo.

AN ARCTIC MIRAGE, occurring when a layer of cool air lies under a warm one, reshapes and vanishes as it is approached (*opposite*). From a distance (*top*), rocks appear in a channel off the Labrador coast. Closer up (*center*), two separate images are formed; then both disappear (*bottom*). Such a mirage reflects real but far-distant rocks.

2

The Slow
Conquest
of the North

IN the lifetime of people born in this century the summit of the globe
has become almost a commonplace: at 20,000 feet it can be crossed as
casually as the equator. Today the high goal that dizzies exploratory minds
is no longer the North Pole, nor any place on earth, no longer a glacial
fastness but the spatial vastness beyond earth. In the cradles of civilization,
however, there was a long period when man did not even suspect the poles
existed, let alone surmise that they were cold. There was a long, later time
when he knew only that the Arctic was there, and full of nameless terrors.
Still later he shrewdly conceived it as a theoretical means to an end, a
short cut to the wealth of the east. Not until over a century ago did the
exploration of the far north become a pressing challenge to the questing
human spirit. Yet even in antiquity, it seems to have beckoned a few
imaginative souls.

Although he probably did not penetrate the Arctic Circle, a Greek
named Pytheas can be called the first arctic explorer. After a northern
voyage Pytheas returned about 325 B.C. to Massilia, the Greek colony at
the site of Marseilles, and like any good explorer he had a journal. All

that survived of it were a few sentences quoted in ancient literature to show how unreliable Pytheas was. But from these quotations it is known that he sailed westward in the Mediterranean, passed through the Strait of Gibraltar and headed north, reaching England and later Scotland. From there he went to a place called *Ultima Thule*. He reported that in Thule bees were kept and honey was produced; in midsummer the nights in Thule lasted only two or three hours; people from Scotland made the trip to Thule once in a while; and such a voyage took six days.

What was *Ultima Thule*, the "outermost land"? The Irish monk Dicuil wrote in about A.D. 825 that other Irish monks had discovered a large island far to the northwest—modern Iceland. Dicuil took it for granted that this was the land reached by Pytheas and for this reason called it Thule.

It was the scholarly Norwegian explorer Fridtjof Nansen who some 50 years ago doubted the time-honored identification of Iceland with Thule. In a carefully reasoned explanation Nansen pointed out that Thule must have been Norway, specifically the area around Trondheim. This now-widely-accepted theory rolls back antiquity's "farthest north" to a point barely halfway up the coast of Norway. Nonetheless the voyage of Pytheas is a landmark of history, the first northern expedition made by somebody who could write about it.

THE next inkling of the Arctic comes from a source which is both surprising and difficult to evaluate, the St. Brendan's Saga. St. Brendan was born in A.D. 484, in County Kerry, later became abbot of the monastery Cluain Fearta in Galway, and died in 577 at the age of 93. His saga is mainly fiction. But one item is of interest—that St. Brendan encountered a "floating crystal castle" on the high seas. This is now taken to be a poetic allusion to sighting an iceberg, and if so is the first mention of an iceberg in literature.

But again, St. Brendan may or may not have penetrated the Arctic himself. Fittingly the first one who definitely did was a Norseman by the name of Ohthere or Ottar. In about 870 he rounded the North Cape, Scandinavia's northernmost point, and sailed east into what is now called the Barents Sea, followed the coastal line of the Kola Peninsula and discovered the White Sea, which he entered. This was the first recorded voyage into true polar waters. Norsemen also crossed the western ocean. In the Ninth Century they reached and took over Iceland, where they found a small colony of Irish monks. Soon after, one viking, blown off his course as he sailed for Iceland, saw land "westward across the main."

That chance discovery of more land might not have borne fruit but for the nasty and uncontrollable temper of one of the Icelandic settlers. He was Eirik Raude (Eric the Red), who had killed several men in brawls. After one outbreak of bloodshed Eric and his men were declared outlaws and forced to leave Iceland. It was then that the story of more land to the northwest was remembered. Eric set sail for it.

Many days' sail to the west Eric sighted the snow-clad peaks of an unknown island. For three years he explored the coast, before returning briefly to Iceland, probably in 985. "Greenland" was the name he gave the new land to make it sound attractive. He announced that he would return there to found a colony; anybody was welcome to come along. The call for volunteers was a big success, for when the Norsemen set out on the trip their

WILLEM BARENTS (1560-1597), Dutch navigator, made the most important arctic discoveries of the 16th Century while seeking a Northeast Passage from the North Atlantic through the Arctic Ocean to the Pacific.

● On his first voyage in 1594 he sailed north of Scandinavia and penetrated the Kara Sea without being stopped by ice. This was the farthest penetration of the Arctic Ocean up to that time. Part of his route is called the Barents Sea.

● He might have reached the Pacific on his third voyage in 1596 but turned too far north and became locked in the ice. He and his crew became the first Europeans ever to pass a winter in the Arctic.

● He escaped the ice with most of his men the next spring but died, at 37, of exposure while making his way to land. The accuracy of his charts was remarkable and greatly aided later explorers.

fleet numbered 25 ships. Only 14 reached their destination and the settlement called *Østerbygd* ("eastern settlement") was founded on the southwest coast of Greenland. A second settlement, called *Vesterbygd* ("western settlement") later was established farther north along the coast.

For nearly 500 years there were flourishing Norse settlements in Greenland. Monasteries and nunneries were established, there was trade with Europe and tithes were even collected by the Pope. Then, mysteriously, these settlements disappeared. One theory is that they were absorbed by Eskimos, another that the climate entered a cold phase and that the *Knarren*, the annual relief and supply ship from Norway, may have come less and less frequently, often missing a number of years in a row at certain critical periods, and that the Greenlanders perished.

The period of the Norse explorations lasted over four centuries. During this time the Norsemen sailed their long boats to all coasts from Newfoundland and Labrador in the west to Novaya Zemlya in the east. But they were a people in a backwater of civilization; it took Columbus' discovery of the New World to alter the course of history's main stream.

The familiar date of 1492 is as important in arctic exploration as it is in American history. The purpose of Columbus' voyage was not to find a new continent but to open up an easy sea route from Europe to the Orient. Columbus of course did not land on the North American continent itself on this voyage, but rather on the islands of the West Indies. But in his wake came several other explorations which soon determined the general outlines of the North American continent. This huge land mass quickly turned out to be a nuisance, an obstacle in the way of the route to the riches of the east. Thus began the search for the "North-West Passage."

VITUS JONASSEN BERING (1681-1741), a Dane, spent 36 years exploring for Russia and made the greatest arctic trips of the 18th Century. His last voyage, in 1741, established Russia's claim to Alaska.

● In 1725, Bering trekked 5,000 miles across Russia to his ships on the Pacific coast. During the subsequent voyage he discovered several arctic islands, charted the Kamchatka Peninsula and sailed through the passage between Alaska and Siberia, now called the Bering Strait.

● In 1734, Bering was to start a second voyage—but was held up for six years by administrative delays. Once at sea, he charted vast sectors of the northern Russian coast line and landed in Alaska.

● In 1741, this voyage ended in disaster when the ship ran aground and Bering died of scurvy. His crew buried him by strapping his body to a plank and shoving it into soft sand till the body sank.

IN 1577 Queen Elizabeth saw Sir Martin Frobisher off on a voyage to China via the Northwest Passage. Frobisher wound up at the head of an elongated bay, now known as Frobisher Bay, and had to turn back. He was also distracted by the discovery of what he thought was a huge gold deposit—and returned to England with a sample of shiny iron pyrites, to be hailed as the hapless discoverer of "fool's gold." The explorer Henry Hudson, probing northwestward in 1610 in the pay of English businessmen, found the strait and large bay which bear his name. Such men as John Davis and William Baffin probed still deeper into the ice in a vain search for a way around America.

Then for a long time the search was all but abandoned because difficult conditions seemed to bar any opening of a trade route to Asia. In the 18th Century the spread of the Russians across Siberia served to disclose the northern coasts of the Asian continent; but these Russian discoveries only dispelled hopes of developing a Northeast Passage by sea to the Orient.

Toward the end of the 18th Century, the great Pacific navigator Captain James Cook returned from a voyage to the Bering Strait to report he could find no ice-free ways into the Arctic to either east or west. By then explorers were coming to the reluctant conclusion that they would never find a way across the north by avoiding the ice, and that the only hope was to force a way through the pack. By sticking it out through winter ice, the British navigator Edward Parry almost penetrated through the Northwest Passage in 1819 before running into impassable ice in the last narrow channel northwest of the Canadian mainland. The British government spurred new efforts by posting two large rewards—£20,000 for finding the Northwest Passage, and £5,000 for the first ship to reach a latitude of 89°.

Of all the names connected with subsequent 19th Century polar exploration, none is more fateful than that of Sir John Franklin. In 1844 the British Admiralty, believing that the new, propeller-driven steamships of the day at last provided the means of cracking the ice of the Northwest Passage, put Sir John in command of the strongest, best-equipped arctic expedition up to that time. His ships were the three-masted barks, H.M.S. *Erebus* (370 tons) and H.M.S. *Terror* (340 tons), newly fitted with steam engines, propellers that could be retracted clear of the ice if necessary, and—unheard-of luxury—an intricate system of hot-water pipes to warm the cabins.

At 59, Sir John was a controversial figure in English political society, but he did have considerable arctic experience. The expedition he led was the first of a series of 19th Century voyages to suffer from incredible bad luck. Not one of the 129 officers and men aboard the two ships ever returned to civilization. The ships were quickly caught in crushing ice. In the second winter scurvy took the life of Sir John. After the third winter his second-in-command abandoned ship and led the surviving 105 officers and men south across the ice-packed straits. These men were not equipped for the trip: they had no guns for hunting, but did insist on lugging their silver cutlery because it bore the royal monogram. In due course the rest of the world sensed disaster. Public opinion was aroused. In one of the greatest searches in history, all kinds of rescue efforts were launched, many of them stimulated by the tireless exertions of Franklin's second wife, Jane, who was certain that her redoubtable husband was still alive.

It fell to the Scottish explorer John Rae to make the grim discovery that eventually caused the British Admiralty to abandon further searches. Ranging north through Canada's arctic archipelago after hearing from Eskimos that a party of white men had been seen hauling small boats toward the Great Fish River (now Back River), he ultimately found the frozen remains of 30 of Franklin's men. No other bodies were ever found. Altogether, no fewer than 40 expeditions took part in the long hunt and, in piecing together the story of the Franklin disaster, the searchers found out more about the North American Arctic in the single decade from 1850 to 1860 than had been discovered in the previous 200 years.

AND yet the area around the pole itself was still a mystery. No one had ever seen it or even been close to it. An urge to reach the pole began to grow, and by 1879 it was strong enough to encourage Lieutenant George Washington De Long of the United States Navy to drift north with the pack ice in the hope of touching any land lying at or near the pole.

His expedition, which was to be mounted in the 142-foot, three-masted bark *Jeannette*, was sponsored by James Gordon Bennett, proprietor of the New York *Herald*. Bennett was well aware of the prestige and circulation such support and the promise of exclusive stories would bring to his paper. He had already had notable success in 1872, by commissioning Stanley to find Livingstone in Africa, and in 1873, by sponsoring an expedition to search for Franklin relics. When the *Jeannette* cleared San Francisco on July 8, 1879, the crew was as optimistic as Sir John Franklin's men had been sailing down the river Thames 34 years earlier. Bennett had spent some $100,000 rebuilding the ship, formerly the yacht *Pandora*, at the

Mare Island Navy Yard. *Jeannette's* bow was bolstered by 10 feet of solid oak and pine, her sides were thickened with planking to a depth of more than 20 inches. Solid oak beams, 12 by 14 inches, were laid athwartships to withstand any conceivable pressure.

Captain De Long was, in the words of his young bride, Emma, a man of "indomitable energy, strong will and passion for overcoming obstacles." He was soon put severely to the test on all counts. Near Herald Island, which he had chosen as the place to begin his long drift north, the *Jeannette* met heavy ice floes. By September 6 she was solidly frozen in the pack. De Long tried everything to free her: using his engines at full speed, shifting ballast, warping the hull with deck winches and cables, even blasting the ice with explosives. The ship refused to budge.

TWENTY months passed. The ship had moved barely over 300 miles from her original position. "We are drifting about like a modern Flying Dutchman," wrote the frustrated De Long. Then, just before midnight on June 10, 1881, De Long was violently awakened by a series of earthquakelike shocks jarring his ship from stem to stern. Rushing to the deck, he saw a space of open water widening slowly around his battered ship. For a few hours he hoped that he might at last be free, that his 32 people "wearing out their souls like men doomed" could sail for home again. Then the ice began to close in, tightening around the hapless *Jeannette* like a mighty vise. The bow buckled, the seams opened, the ship tilted crazily. Two days later, De Long ordered her abandoned.

Most of the supplies already had been removed. De Long had ample equipment for 33 men: three boats, six sledges, 23 dogs and rations for 60 days. The expedition set out, heading due south toward Siberia. It was summer, the worst possible season for sledging. The snow was too soft for runners. The men constantly slipped into pools of slush that soaked them through and through; the heaving pack reared barrier after barrier of jagged ice across their path. After one week of this ordeal, De Long made a horrifying discovery: though he had managed to advance over the ice at a rate of four miles a day, the drift of ocean currents had meanwhile carried the pack so far to the north that their position was now 28 miles farther from their Siberian goal than when they had set out.

Sharing this appalling news only with two of his officers, De Long resolutely changed course from south to southwest. De Long figured that this heading would bring him to the edge of the ice pack, where the party could take to the boats and sail for the Siberian coast. An idea of the vast scope of this plan can be gained by considering that the distance to be covered equaled one third the breadth of the United States; that the equipment to be hauled over ice weighed almost eight tons; and that one out of three men was too sick to do anything but drag himself along.

Yet they did reach open water. One boat capsized and all aboard were lost. One eventually reached the safety of a Siberian village. In the third, De Long and his own party finally landed near the mouth of the Lena River on September 17, 1881, with a four-day supply of rations left. The men were badly frostbitten. Yet De Long, maintaining astonishing discipline, gave orders to march south. By October 8, his party was down to 13 men, and the commander himself was almost too weak to go on. He decided the only remaining hope was to send two men ahead to try to find help.

SIR JOHN FRANKLIN (1786-1847) was the tragic hero of arctic exploration. In 1846 he sailed into the Victoria Channel, adding to the chain of discoveries that established the Northwest Passage.

● Franklin's two ships lay trapped for two years in a welter of ice that jammed the channel. He and his 128 men died of scurvy, hunger and exhaustion despite a desperate attempt to escape to the south.

● Franklin's disappearance inspired a lengthy search for survivors or evidence of the expedition's fate. Lady Franklin herself sent four ships; she based her instructions to the captains on a mysterious map revealed by the spirit of a four-year-old girl, Weesy Coppin, who had recently died in Ireland. Later expeditions found the map had accurately indicated the spot where Franklin died.

The two men actually reached civilization. Half conscious and raving incoherently, they stumbled upon a native camp and were taken to the Russian settlement of Bulun. Search parties were sent out, but could not find the rest of the party. It was not until next spring that De Long was found. Near his body was the logbook he had desperately protected, with the grim record of the ordeal from the time of leaving the *Jeannette* in mid-Arctic until the last tragic entry 140 days later. De Long failed in his intention, to reach the pole, but he succeeded in writing one of the classic records of arctic endeavor, with the final, almost unintelligible scrawl: "Oct. 30, Sun. 140th day. Boyd and Gortz died during night. Mr. Collins dying."

As De Long and his men met their end in 1881, Austrian scientists were carrying out plans for an ambitious polar project, the First International Polar Year. The purpose of the Polar Year of 1882-1883 was not to try to set records or reach the poles, but to gather scientific data at remote outposts and to keep detailed records, over a 12-month period, on the weather, climatic changes and other phenomena of geophysical interest. Fifteen parties (11 arctic and four antarctic) were sent to predetermined locations. Thirty-four permanent observatories in many countries also took part.

IT was an International Polar Year expedition that contributed the third chapter of misfortune in 19th Century arctic history. One of two sent out by the United States, it came under the supervision of the Army and is known as the Greely Expedition, after its commander, Major Adolphus W. Greely. Its story was one of unrelieved tragedy in the field and preposterous mismanagement by those who governed the relief parties.

In the summer of 1881 the expedition was transported by the small ship *Proteus* to its station at Discovery Harbor high up on Ellesmere Island, the northernmost outpost of 15 such stations. Under Greely were two lieutenants, a doctor, 10 sergeants, a corporal, nine privates and two Eskimo hunters from nearby Greenland.

Once the camp was established the *Proteus* sailed for home. To guard against disaster to the 26 isolated men, the United States government had set up a carefully detailed plan. In 1882 a relief ship would be dispatched to the station. Even if it should fail to get through because of ice, there would be no cause for alarm, for the Greely party had supplies for more than two years. In any event, a second ship would set out in the summer of 1883; but if it, too, should fail to reach the base, it would send a relief mission over the ice to rescue the explorers.

All went well at Discovery Harbor at first. Living conditions were excellent, and during the summer months the land was covered with grass and flowers and abundant with game. But two factors contributed to disharmony: Greely was an unpopular leader, and three of his men—an officer, a sergeant and the expedition doctor—were fractious to the point of insubordination. The group still carried out its planned observations. It also tried to reach one other objective—completely out of keeping with the spirit of the International Polar Year: to make a try for the pole, or at least to better the exploratory record. The record just then was a position near the 83rd parallel, off Ellesmere Island, reached by Lieutenant Albert Markham of the British Arctic Expedition of 1875-1876.

In this effort, the Greely Expedition was successful. Three of the major's party reached 83° 24′ lat. N., some four miles beyond the point attained by Markham. This success was almost inconsequential, in view of the disaster that was to follow.

The second winter having passed with no sign of a relief party, Greely decided to retreat south. For his 25 men, he had a steam launch and a whaleboat. On August 9, 1883, they broke camp. The party was in good physical condition, but torn by violent disagreements. The situation had become so out-of-hand that Greely had arrested the physician, Dr. Octave Pavy, for insubordination. There were open arguments as to the best route southward. The destination was finally determined to be Cape Sabine, some 200 miles away, where there was a cache of supplies.

Storms hammered their two boats and their rations dwindled, but the party neared Cape Sabine. Greely was confident that they would have little further trouble; he was counting on extensive stores which the Army was to have set up along the routes of retreat. He did not count on neglect and disinterest on the part of government administrators. Though relief expeditions had carried some 50,000 rations into the area in the two preceding summers, only 1,000 were ever cached where Greely could get them. The rest were either lost when a relief ship, the *Proteus*, was crushed in the ice, or else brought back to the United States.

For eight all-but-intolerable months the Greely party huddled under an inverted lifeboat on Bedford Pym Island, off Cape Sabine. Repeated scouting expeditions to try to locate the food caches only served to exhaust the men. The two Eskimos lost their lives trying to find game and fish for the party. The rest were reduced to eating seaweed, lichens, sand fleas and even leather thongs. By the first week in June 1884 Greely was the only surviving officer. There was one noncom left, and six privates. Greely ordered one of the privates shot for stealing from the food supply—now so pitiful that on June 15 Greely's log recorded: "The sleeping bag cover roasted and boiled to suit each one . . . the last of the skin divided today."

But after outrageous bumbling, rescue was on its way. It was the grim lot of Captain W. S. Schley, later the victor over the Spanish in the Battle of Santiago Bay, to locate the seven pathetic survivors of the expedition, still huddled together at Cape Sabine.

"He was a ghastly sight," Schley wrote later in his account of coming upon the first of Greely's men. "His cheeks were hollow, his eyes wild, his hair and beard long and matted."

His meeting with Greely was more gruesome. Opening the torn flap of a makeshift tent, he stared, first, straight into the glassy eyes of a dead man. "Directly opposite," wrote Schley, "on his hands and knees was a dark man with a long matted beard, in a dirty and tattered dressing gown, with a little red skull cap on his head. . . . The man made no answer, staring vacantly. . . . One of the men spoke up, 'That's the Major—Major Greely.'"

Greely finally managed to speak. He had only one thing to say, and he said it: "Did what I came to do—beat the best record." Then he fell back exhausted. Nursed back to health, Greely survived, to become a major general by his death in 1935.

If the Franklin, *Jeannette* and Greely expeditions were classic examples of failure, the next major one was an outstanding success. This was the *Fram* expedition, ably led by Norway's Dr. Nansen in 1893. Looking back, as he made his plans, Dr. Nansen could be thankful that he was equipped

FREDERICK A. COOK (1865-1940), a quiet American doctor, claimed he discovered the North Pole in 1908, a year before Peary got there on April 6, 1909.

● Cook had a reputation as an explorer with experience in both the Arctic and Antarctic. He left Greenland with nine Eskimos on February 19, 1908. For a year and a half, no one knew where he was. Then, five days before Peary returned with the news of his own success, Cook reappeared and announced he had reached the pole the year before.

● Cook was soon challenged. Peary said he had "handed the public a gold brick." The Explorers' Club said Cook had lied about an earlier exploit. Investigations found little support for Cook's claim. In 1923 he was convicted of mail fraud in oil-stock sales. He was later pardoned, but died bitter and discredited.

with much knowledge that his ill-fated predecessors had lacked only a decade earlier. The First International Polar Year had contributed much meteorological data to arctic lore. Greely's expedition had shown that a party must be self-sufficient, and not count on outside help. The *Jeannette* saga had contributed the most vital information of all, by virtually disproving the theory that there was a "polar continent"; it had shown how rapidly the ice pack traveled in a vast circular motion around the Arctic seas. The ambitious goal Nansen set for himself was this: to drift to a high latitude—or to the pole itself—in a ship deliberately frozen solidly into the pack.

He based his plan on the washing up of Siberian driftwood on the shores of Greenland, on the drift of the icebound *Jeannette*, and on one other priceless fact furnished by the *Jeannette* expedition—a fact not recorded in that heroic logbook kept by De Long. This was the discovery, three years after the *Jeannette* had been crushed by the ice, of part of its wreckage on the southwest coast of Greenland, on the very opposite side of the polar basin. If wreckage, frozen in the moving ice, had drifted right around the pole from the Asian side to the Atlantic side, why couldn't a well-designed ship do the same thing?

On the 24th of June, 1893, the *Fram* ("Forward"), under the command of Captain Otto Sverdrup, took Nansen eastward out of Norway. The ship had been designed to withstand enormous pressures on her hull. She was shaped so that, like a watermelon seed, she would be squeezed right up out of the ice if the pressure became too great, and would then sink down again as the pressure eased.

North of the Lena Delta, at 77° 44′ lat. N., Nansen and Sverdrup ran the ship deep into the pack ice until all forward motion stopped. As planned, the ice lifted the ship, which rode on an even keel. But by March 1895 it was clear that the drift northwestward was not going to take the ship across the pole, so Nansen decided on a daring undertaking. On March 14, he left the considerable comforts of the *Fram* and with one companion, Hjalmar Johansen, and dogs, sledges, two kayaks and food for 100 days, struck northward across the jagged ice floes.

"Ridge after ridge, and nothing but rubble to travel over," wrote Nansen in the meticulous diary of his expedition, "and from the highest hummock only the same kind of ice was to be seen. It was a veritable chaos of ice-blocks, stretching as far as the horizon."

They sledged northward until April 8. Then the onset of warm weather compelled them to turn around. At that point Nansen and his companion had reached 86° 14′ N., only 224 nautical miles from the pole. It was man's farthest north penetration in the 19th Century. The two explorers headed south and by the end of August, reaching Franz Josef Land, decided to hole up there for the winter.

Living on the meat and blubber of the bears and walruses they shot, Nansen and Johansen spent the next eight months in a crude stone hut. In May 1896 they headed south again, finally meeting the Jackson-Harmsworth Expedition. By coincidence, the *Fram* was breaking out of the ice north of Spitsbergen on August 13 of that year, the same day on which Nansen and Johansen landed in Norway. The stout little ship sailed back to Tromsö, Norway, after a voyage of more than 35 months, without the loss of a single man. The Nansen expedition had been carried to a tri-

VILHJALMUR STEFANSSON (1879-), American anthropologist of Icelandic ancestry, studied ways of Eskimo life and learned to live for long periods in the Arctic without relying on supplies of food or fuel from the outside.

● Stefansson used these techniques to make long journeys through northern Canada. He led the Canadian Arctic Expedition of 1913-1918, which mapped large areas of unexplored territory.

● Stefansson set up the first scientific station on a drifting ice floe in 1918. For eight months his party made regular observations of ice and tides while they floated more than 400 miles in the Beaufort Sea. Since 1937, both the Soviet Union and the United States have maintained similar stations on the huge "ice islands" floating in the Arctic Ocean.

umphant end. As Nansen predicted, no new land had been found in the far north. The *Fram* had drifted from the Siberian coast to $85°\ 55'$ N. at its highest position and emerged on the Atlantic side of the arctic basin. Nansen had become the first to penetrate the heart of the Arctic. The ocean itself proved to be quite deep; numerous soundings through the ice had established that the polar sea was at least 2,000 fathoms deep and seemed to get even deeper in the direction of the North Pole.

By this time, at the turn of the century, the exploration of the north had turned into a race for the pole. Where might the best vantage point of land be from which to start the last dash to the position where all lines of longitude merge? The *Jeannette* story had seemed to destroy the chance that there was land north of the Siberian offshore islands. Nansen's drift had disposed of the probability of land in the high latitudes north of Europe. The question remained whether there might be land extending north of Greenland toward the pole.

One man had spent his life finding the answer to this question in the consuming conviction that he was the one person on earth destined to conquer the North Pole. Dedicated and determined, Robert E. Peary was a new kind of polar explorer. The earlier ones, men like Henry Hudson and John Davis, had held the polar winter in such fear that they only made quick northward incursions by ship in summer and then withdrew. A later generation, of whom Edward Parry was a notable example, had dreaded the cold of polar winter, but was made of such stern stuff that it would brave its terrors, dig in and wait for summer's return. Peary broke away from these notions in his belief that an arctic winter, far from being dreadful, is the best season for exploring—even better than summer, when the surface of the ice pack thaws and the going is rough. He was also a strong believer in using dogs and Eskimo clothing, and in traveling light but carrying along all of an expedition's own food.

For over 20 years Peary had been forming these ideas in the course of becoming an expert on travel on Greenland ice. Twice he successfully crossed the Greenland ice sheet. In 1900 he discovered Greenland's northern extremity—now named Peary Land. In 1906 he worked his way from Ellesmere Island to $87°\ 06'$ N., only 170 miles from the pole and farther than any man had ever penetrated before. To him, the finding of the long-sought Northwest Passage by Roald Amundsen in 1906 was a matter of utter indifference. He had steeled his will to one purpose: to reach the pole itself. That prize he would take in the certainty that it was the summit of his life's achievement. Discoveries that men like Nansen had made Peary dismissed with the remark that such people had "not hit the exact center of the bull's-eye."

In July 1908 Peary sailed in the *Roosevelt* for his jumping-off point on the north tip of Ellesmere Island, 413 miles from the pole. On the outward march he took with him six men, including the ship's master, Robert ("Captain Bob") Bartlett; a surgeon, Dr. J. W. Goodsell; his secretary, Ross Marvin; and two young explorers, George Borup and Donald Macmillan. The sixth member was Matthew Henson, the Negro aide who had accompanied him on previous marches across the ice. They were supported by 17 Eskimos, with 133 dogs.

"My theory was to work the supporting parties to the limit," Peary re-

SIR HUBERT WILKINS (1888-1958), an Australian pioneer of modern methods of arctic travel, was the first to cross the Arctic Ocean in an airplane and the first to try to reach the pole in a submarine.

● In 1928, Wilkins flew 2,000 miles from Point Barrow in Alaska to Spitsbergen, a flight financed by a group of Detroit businessmen who foresaw the possibilities of commercial transpolar flights.

● In 1931, Wilkins sailed from Spitsbergen aboard a U.S. submarine in an attempt to reach the pole by going under the worst of the ice. Violent storms damaged the boat's diving gear and forced him to turn back after three weeks, but the observations made on his voyage resulted in a much better understanding of the movements of the currents and the ice pack of the Arctic Ocean.

called in his book, *The North Pole*, "in order to keep the main party fresh; and those men who I expected from the beginning to form the main party at the last had things made as easy as possible for them all the way up." It was a sound program, similar to the platoon system now used in scaling the highest mountain peaks. Peary also decided to keep his final party as small as possible. The larger the unit, he knew, the slower it could go forward.

Gradually, during the northward trek, supporting parties were sent back, always consisting of the least useful Eskimos and dogs. On April 1, 1909, Bob Bartlett and the last supporting party turned south, just 133 nautical miles from the pole. In the final party there were only Peary, Matt Henson and four Eskimos. The weather was fine.

"Give me three more days of this weather!" wrote Peary in his diary. With his five strong, experienced men, he set the stiff quota of 25 miles a day for the final sprint. Everything went well.

"The last march northward ended at 10 o'clock on the forenoon of April 6. I had now made the five marches planned from the point at which Bartlett turned back, and my reckoning showed that we were in the immediate neighborhood of the goal of all our striving."

His position turned out to be 89° 57′ N.

"Yet," continued Peary, "with the Pole actually in sight I was too weary to take the last few steps. . . .I was actually too exhausted to realize at the moment that my life's purpose had been achieved."

He forced himself and his men across the last stretch of ice. Then:

"The Pole at last. The prize of three centuries. My dream and goal for 20 years. Mine at last!"

The conquest was such an exhausting experience that all he wanted to do was to lie down and sleep, which he did for about three hours.

For another 30 hours—taking soundings through the ice, making weather observations and resting—they stayed at the point from which the only direction is south. Their return journey was easy as arctic forays went. The snowhouses built on the way north were ready to shelter the six men; the tracks made by the returning support parties were generally visible. On April 25, Peary boarded the *Roosevelt* in triumph. The final conquest of the Arctic had seemed so absurdly simple.

AFTER Peary's triumph, other feats inevitably were achieved, such as Admiral Richard E. Byrd's first flight over the pole and back, and Roald Amundsen's crossing of the arctic basin in a dirigible in 1926, which made him the first man to attain both poles.

A dedicated North Dakotan of Icelandic descent, Vilhjalmur Stefansson, took the view that the north was not nearly as unfriendly as others thought, and that a trained hunter could live off the land. In the course of a five-year period he and two companions disappeared over the ice to the north with no supplies other than guns and ammunition. During his travels he discovered the last remaining land masses in the Northern Hemisphere.

The long record of questing valor and ingenuity in the face of unknown terrors, the history that began with Pytheas's Norwegian journey, was closed with Peary's polar march. Today, planes fly daily over the point that Peary fought and finally claimed for his own. Man has indeed become master of the Arctic, but he has many earlier men to thank for it.

FLANKED BY FLAGS, PEARY PREPARES HIS SEXTANT FOR OBSERVATIONS SHOWING HE HAD REACHED 90° NORTH—"THE POLE AT LAST"

Peary's "Great Prize"

For the American explorer Robert Peary, gaining the North Pole was "the fixed purpose of my life." Repeatedly turned back for 20 years, he made a final attempt in 1908. "I knew," he wrote, "it was win this time or be forever defeated." Beginning on this page, an album of the pictures taken on that expedition shows how Peary won the "last great prize."

BASE FOR THE WINTER is aboard the *Roosevelt*, frozen fast in the coastal ice north of Cape Sheridan. It was dynamited free for the trip home.

FURS FOR THE COLD are stitched together into garments that kept men warm in -50° blizzards. The women chewed each skin to make it soft.

FOOD FOR THE DOGS comes from catch such as this two-tusked narwhal (*left*), harpooned and shot when it surfaced for air. Most narwhals have one tusk.

Preparing at Cape Sheridan

On a sweltering day in July 1908, Peary's stubby, black-hulled S.S. *Roosevelt* steamed out of New York and headed north. A few weeks later she cruised along the west coast of Greenland, picking up a deckload of 150 tons of ripe whale and walrus flesh, 246 snarling dogs and 49 excited Eskimo men, women and children. Then she nosed cautiously into the ice-choked passage between Greenland and Ellesmere Island. After battering through loose floes for 350 miles, she finally made fast to the ice off Cape Sheridan—500 miles from the pole—on September 5.

Already the Eskimos were building sledges and making fur garments for the polar push. As twilight deepened into winter darkness, hunting parties headed inland tracking caribou and musk oxen, and heavily loaded sledges began moving up the coast to an advance base at Cape Columbia, 90 miles northwest, where Peary would start his final march to the pole in the spring.

POWER FOR THE SLEDGES, dogs able to carry supplies "where no other power on earth could have moved them" surround Peary on the *Roosevelt*.

MEAT FOR THE TABLE and skins for clothing and sleeping robes are piled on sledges as the hunters return after bagging a supply of caribou (*below*).

A GNAWING BABY happily makes a greasy mess of his furs and himself (*left*) as he strips raw caribou meat from an old bone. He was one of 10 children who went along on the *Roosevelt*.

A GIGGLING CHORUS runs through a music hall song-and-dance number (*below*) learned from the crew. Dubbed "The Floradora Sextet," the girls before long could do a spirited cancan.

A WRESTLING PAIR of hunters (*below*) strain to throw each other off balance. When an Eskimo won such a test of strength, he would sometimes claim the loser's wife.

Peary's "Strange and Faithful" Friends

To the 225 Eskimos scattered along the shore of Smith Sound in northwest Greenland, Peary was a demanding and respected friend. For 18 years he had relied on the skills and endurance of "these strange and faithful people" to help him cross the unexplored wastes of northern Greenland and push closer and closer to the pole. They supplied his sledges and dogs, furs and food, and were the sledge drivers, hunters and trail breakers on every important expedition he led. "I have grown to love this childlike, simple people," Peary wrote. "Every individual member of the tribe is known to me by name and sight. I have saved whole villages from starvation, and the children are taught by their parents that if they grow up and become good hunters or seamstresses, 'Pearyaksoah' [Big Peary] will reward them . . . in the not too distant future."

AN ICE BARRIER, thrust up by violent shifts in the pack, is surmounted when sledges are hauled up steep paths cut with pickaxes.

The Struggle across the Ice

The returning sun was glowing dimly below the horizon when Peary marshaled his sledge forces at Cape Columbia—500 miles from the pole—in late February, 1909. There were 24 men, 133 dogs and 19 sledges with 6,500 pounds of supplies. Most of the party he organized into supporting divisions, whose sole function was to bring his own six-man group within striking distance of the pole with enough dogs, food and energy for the final dash. On March 1, Peary left the shore and set out across the ice pack. The following weeks he later described as a time of "forced marches, physical discomfort, insufficient sleep and racking anxiety." Travel was brutally hard. The surface of the ice was contorted by the pressure of wind and current into jagged ridges and hummocks as much as 60 feet high. More harassing were the "leads"—lanes of open water that formed without warning. One lead delayed Peary six days as he waited for it to close. He crossed others by having rafts chopped from the floes or by inching over the thin film of ice that soon covered them in the -40° air. But by the end of March, Peary was only 133 miles from the pole.

A CHILLY SHELTER built of packed snow is littered
with gear after an overnight stop. Inside
such igloos the temperature was often below zero.

A MAKESHIFT RAFT chopped out of the ice (*below*)
serves as a ferryboat to carry an Eskimo driver,
his dogs and a loaded sledge across a lead of open water.

MATT HENSON, PEARY'S COMPANION TO THE POLE

At the Pole: "Three Rousing Cheers"

On April 1, the last of Peary's supporting divisions turned back. For his final sprint, Peary kept the best of the dogs, four picked Eskimos and a 43-year-old Negro, Matthew Henson, a trusted companion of 20 years of arctic exploring and one of the finest sledge drivers in the north.

With clear weather and across relatively unbroken ice they raced north, stopping only briefly for food and rest. Peary himself, who had lost his toes after his feet were frostbitten during a crossing of Ellesmere Island in 1899, was able to keep up only by riding most of the distance in one of the sledges.

Finally, at 10 a.m. on April 6, Peary called a halt: he was at the goal. He built an igloo. Then he produced a silk-taffeta American flag made by his wife, tied it to a stick and planted it atop the igloo. After making sextant observations to confirm his position, he "turned in for a few hours of absolutely necessary sleep." Later there was a short ceremony. Peary photographed his men holding an array of flags (*right*), Henson led the Eskimos in "three rousing cheers" and everyone shook hands. Wrote Peary: "I am content."

PEARY'S STANDARDS at the pole (*right*) include flags of (*from left*) the Navy League, his fraternity, the U.S., the D.A.R. (its "peace flag") and the Red Cross.

48

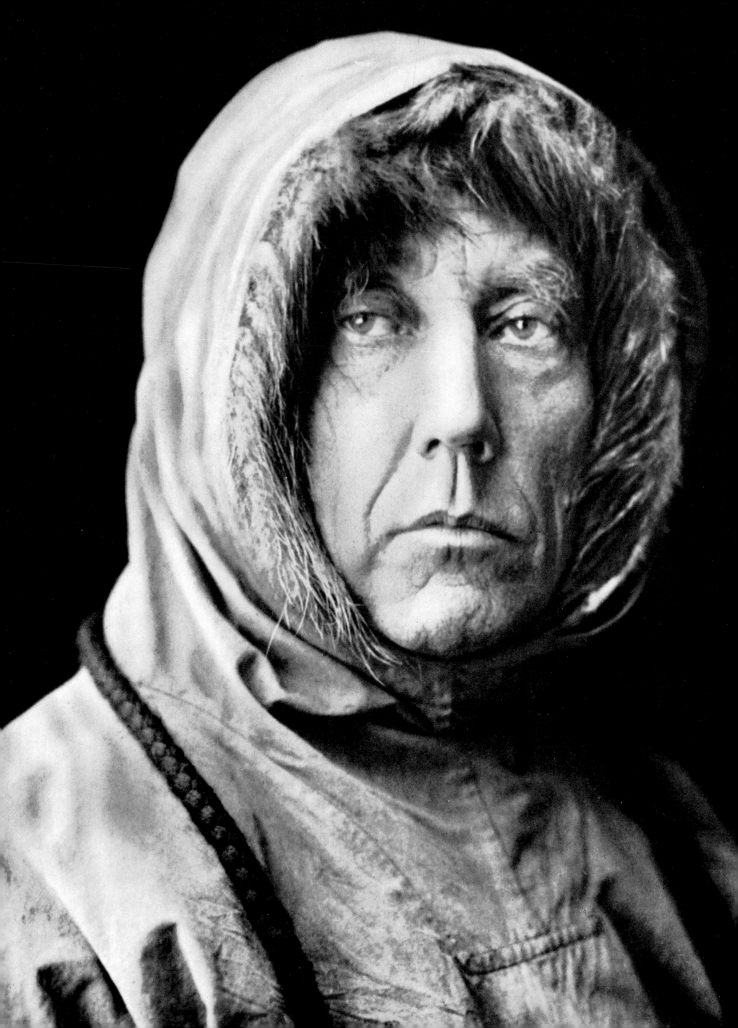

3

Finding the Last Continent

IN man's inexorable occupation of the planet, Antarctica has stood as the
ultimate land frontier. It is the coldest of all seven continents, the most
isolated, the farthest removed from the great centers of human habitation.
It is ringed by the world's stormiest seas, and for most of the year by impenetrable masses of floating ice.

The ancient, logical Greeks, conceiving of the world as a sphere, decided
that in the far south there must be a land mass to balance Europe and Asia
—or else the world would fall over. Then for 2,000 years the very idea of
a global world, with an Arctic at the top offset by an Ant-arctic down
under, was lost. But when Columbus restored the concept, the map makers
put the legendary southern continent, or *terra australis*, back on their maps,
and because it was unknown, added the word *incognita*. Unknown it remained for hundreds of years more, though not unsought.

Generations of sailors hunted the continent in vain. When Magellan discovered the long-desired strait through America to the Pacific in 1520, he
saw land to the south, flickering with the campfires of the natives. He named
it "Fireland," or Tierra del Fuego, believing it to be part of the southern

continent. Voyaging from 1768 to 1771 for the British Admiralty, the great explorer Captain James Cook sailed right around the Antarctic Circle, three times sending his ships beyond it without ever sighting the continent. Finally, in a supreme feat of seamanship, Cook took the 462-ton *Resolution* through gales and pack ice to lat. 71° S., only to come up against solid ice—about 150 miles off the antarctic coast, though he could not know this. Cook believed that no one would ever push farther south, but if someone ever should, he said in his report, "I shall not envy him the fame of his discovery [and] I make bold to declare that the world will derive no benefit from it."

For a long time after that, what little interest men showed in the far south was commercial. In 1819 Czar Alexander I, his taste for exploration sharpened perhaps by Russian successes in Siberian waters, sent an expedition south under Captain Fabian Gottlieb von Bellingshausen. Circling the entire Antarctic, the captain discovered Peter I Island, but the Russians were so disappointed in the voyage that Bellingshausen's excellent reports and charts were not even published until 10 years after his return. It was the wide-ranging sealers and whalers who finally pushed close enough to sight the continent itself. Captain Nathaniel Palmer, a Connecticut sealer, sighted land south of Cape Horn in 1819. His discovery still bears his name and is actually part of the antarctic continent, but Palmer did not know this at the time, nor did rival British whaling captains, one of whom claimed to have discovered Palmer Land three weeks before Palmer did.

The whalers and sealers continued to make sightings. By the 1830s the suspicion grew that the long-lost continent had at last been found, and the British, Americans and French dispatched expeditions southward. Though scientific survey was their avowed purpose, each party had orders to try for record southward penetrations too. First off the mark were the French, led by Jules Dumont d'Urville. The expedition took many measurements of the earth's magnetism in southern waters, and in 1840 d'Urville discovered a bare, rocky shore south of Australia which he called Adélie Land, after his wife.

The American expedition had sailed from Hampton Roads, Virginia, in 1838 under Lieutenant Charles Wilkes of the United States Navy. Apart from magnetic study, its purpose was to establish American claims to at least some part of the Antarctic.

AFTER battling gales and scurvy, and plagued by ships with rotting timbers (he had to use tarred canvas to patch the bulwarks), Wilkes sailed deep into the ice nearest the South Magnetic Pole, sighted a "very long coastline," and followed it for an estimated 1,500 miles. He thus became the first to claim actual discovery of the long-sought antarctic continent.

The British expedition set out in 1841 under the able leadership of James Clark Ross, discoverer of the North Magnetic Pole. Ross started much later than the French and the Americans, but the delay proved an advantage. At his last stop in Hobart, Tasmania, he heard about the islands recently seen by d'Urville and the "very long coastline" followed by Wilkes, and changed his course. This fortunate shift led Ross straight to the discovery of what has proved by far the most accessible coast of the main antarctic continent. He found himself in what is now called the Ross Sea, on the opposite side of the continent from the sealers' haunts in the Palmer Peninsula

NATHANIEL PALMER (1799-1877) was a sea captain from Connecticut who went looking for seals and touched off a geographic dispute that has never been settled. He did not see any seals, but he did find the mainland of Antarctica.

● On a sealing expedition in the South Shetland Islands in 1820, Palmer's ship was sent south to search for more profitable hunting grounds. He sighted an extensive coast, but heavy ice along the shore prevented him from landing.

● On American maps, the land he found is named the Palmer Peninsula. British maps call it Graham Land, and British historians claim that the English explorer Edward Bransfield had visited the same coast some 10 months before. Ironically, Bransfield had seen hundreds of the fur seals that Palmer had gone south to seek.

and the Weddell Sea. Before him rose a line of majestic mountains, to which he gave the name Victoria Land.

"January 27, 1841," Ross wrote in his journal, "discovered a mountain more than 12,400 feet above sea level, emitting flames and smoke in great profusion, a most grand spectacle." A live volcano was the last sight one would expect to see amid all that ice and snow. Ross named it Mount Erebus, after one of his ships. An equally impressive discovery was the Ross Ice Shelf, a part of the continental ice sheet extending hundreds of miles out from the shore. Pushing through Ross Sea ice in 1842, he touched lat. 78° 9′ S., and broke the record for man's southernmost penetration.

After these bold voyages antarctic exploration flagged. Among explorers, the Franklin disaster drew all attention to the north. The Antarctic again was left to the whalers, and it was in fact a Norwegian seaman, one Carstens Borchgrevink, arriving in the Antarctic on a whaling ship, who in 1895 made the first landing on the continent. Borchgrevink climbed the promontory at the entrance of the Ross Sea and became the first man to look down from its top. Later he returned with a small party which became the first to spend an antarctic winter ashore. A Belgian expedition that wintered in the ice off the coast the same year, 1897, was notable for the presence of a man who was making his first antarctic appearance: Roald Amundsen, first mate of the expedition.

THE 20th Century opened the great age of antarctic attainment. The big north-polar problems were solved by then or well on their way to solution, and scientists were urging investigation of the millions of square miles of unexplored land in Antarctica. Specifically, they still wanted some basic magnetic research and, as before, this became the announced goal of three expeditions: one British, one German, one Swedish. This time, however, the expeditions were supported not by the governments but by private grants—for public curiosity about the mysteries of Antarctica had grown intense enough to provide the necessary funds. In August 1901 the British *Discovery* expedition set forth under the leadership of a man whose name will always be coupled with the quest for the South Pole: Commander Robert Falcon Scott. A few days later the Germans watched their hopes go along with geographer Dr. Erich von Drygalski. In October the *Antarctic* sailed from Sweden under the command of Otto Nordenskjöld, nephew of a noted arctic explorer.

During the next two years, all three expeditions concentrated on scientific research rather than discovery. But for Scott, then only 33, these years were a training time for his later explorations. Before going south Scott was not a scientist or tested explorer, but a torpedo specialist. As a disciplined and dedicated young naval officer, however, he had impressed his backers as the kind of leader needed to pioneer in unknown territory. Taking the *Discovery* deep into the Ross Sea, Scott wintered in the mountain-walled shelter of McMurdo Sound. His aim was not to try to reach the South Pole but to experiment with methods for overland exploration across the snows. Finding that sled dogs, so useful in the Arctic, ate too much (there were no game animals to supplement their rations), he tried long marches using man power alone. By the time Scott returned from the *Discovery* expedition in 1904, he was a seasoned polar explorer, deep in plans for a go at the South Pole itself.

FABIAN VON BELLINGSHAUSEN (1779-1852) commanded a Russian naval expedition that circumnavigated the antarctic continent. He sighted part of the mainland in 1820, but he assumed the cliffs he saw were just another ice field.

● Bellingshausen was the first explorer to make an extensive survey in the far south after Captain James Cook's expedition in 1775. Although he did not realize until later that he had seen part of the continent, the Soviet Union today insists he should be credited with the discovery of Antarctica, despite the claims of both Palmer (opposite) and Bransfield.

● Bellingshausen happened to meet Palmer's ship returning from its trip south. He is said to have exclaimed, "We must surrender the palm to you Americans," when Palmer described his find.

JULES DUMONT D'URVILLE (1790-1842), a French ethnologist whose favorite area of study was the semitropical islands of the Pacific, was asked in 1838 by King Louis Philippe to sail to the Antarctic "for the glory of France."

● D'Urville thought his goal ought to be the discovery of the South Magnetic Pole. However, he first tried to obey Louis Philippe's orders to achieve a new "farthest south" in the Weddell Sea.

● D'Urville reached the edge of the Weddell Sea but found the ice pack impenetrable. He retreated to the Pacific.

● D'Urville returned in 1840 and got closer to the magnetic pole than anyone before him. He also sighted what he suspected was land and named it Terre Adélie for his wife; then he sailed on to Côte Claire, named for the wife of one of his captains.

The first man who actually tried to conquer the pole, however, was not Scott but a husky young Irishman who had helped Scott pull the sledges on the first thrust into the antarctic interior. This was Ernest Henry Shackleton who, after running away to sea at 16, had leaped at the chance of more dramatic achievement with Scott in the unknown south. But when Shackleton became weakened from scurvy, Scott called him unfit and sent him home. Shackleton did not forgive this; he vowed he would show Scott and the world that he was not unfit.

Outspoken, romantic, completely self-reliant, Shackleton organized an expedition in 1907 that was aimed at taking both of the grand prizes of antarctic discovery—the South Pole and the South Magnetic Pole. He himself would lead the assault on the pole; a second party, under Professor Edgeworth David of Sydney, was to climb to the icecap and head the other way to the magnetic pole.

Shackleton launched his attack on the pole from McMurdo Sound, near Scott's main base. He had the benefit of all the careful tests by which Scott had determined the best routes, the best rations, the best supply techniques. To pull his sledges across the Ross Ice Shelf and up to the polar plateau, however, Shackleton chose Siberian ponies. These little animals were supposed to be as well accustomed as dogs to cold and hardship. But in the Antarctic, where all provisions must be brought in from outside, they had one big drawback: unlike dogs, they could not eat the same type of food as their masters.

By the time Shackleton was ready to start, in late October 1908, all but four of his ponies had died; and these four were to last only one and a half months. To make the 1,730-mile round trip to the pole and back, the party would have had to cover 14 miles a day—manhauling their sledges almost all the way.

Shackleton gave it a tremendous try. By January 9, 1909, he and three companions had pushed to within nearly 100 miles of the pole. The goal seemed so near, and yet the diary tells how far. January 7: "A blinding, shrieking blizzard all day, with the temperature ranging from -60° to -70° of frost. . . ." January 8: "I feel this march must be our limit. We are so short of food, and at the high altitude, 11,600 feet, it is hard to keep any warmth in our bodies between the scanty meals. . . ." January 9 he wrote: "Our last day outwards. We have shot our bolt, and the tale is latitude 88° 23′ S. . . ."

At 4 o'clock that morning the party made its last dash for the pole, "half running and half walking over a surface much hardened by a recent blizzard." Yet Shackleton knew that though the party might reach the pole, they would lack strength and food to return, and so they turned back. As it was, the four of them almost perished. Again and again they lost their way in blinding blizzards. They were badly frostbitten. They had to fight off snow blindness. One of the ration depots to which they staggered turned out to have no food, only tobacco. Dysentery—probably acquired from eating the cached remains of the last of their ponies—afflicted them. But they won through.

For his 1,700-mile march, hailed as the greatest feat in antarctic exploration, Shackleton was knighted and feted throughout Europe. His second-in-command, Professor David, also received a knighthood; for during the same week Shackleton reached his farthest point south, David's party raised the Union Jack over the South Magnetic Pole.

Shackleton, who died of a heart attack on the island of South Georgia, was a lion of a man. Professor David, 50 years old at the time of the polar trip, was remarkable in quite another way. During this southward traverse, his aide Douglas Mawson—later to become a noted antarctic explorer in his own right—was busy in a tent when he heard David's muffled voice calling:

"Mawson, are you very busy?"

"Yes, I am," replied Mawson, "what's the matter?"

"Are you really *very* busy?"

"Yes," said Mawson, then doing some intricate computation. "What is it you want?"

A moment of silence, then: "Well, I am down a crevasse, and I don't think I can hang on much longer."

The next race to the South Pole was, unfortunately, just that—a race. The unwitting competitors turned out to be Robert F. Scott, who had prepared himself well by his earlier trials, and Roald Amundsen, the conqueror of the Northwest Passage.

Amundsen was an ambitious, determined man, much in the tradition of Ernest Shackleton. In 1909 he was planning to head for the North Pole in Fridtjof Nansen's famous ship *Fram*, when he heard that Robert E. Peary had gotten there first. At once, Amundsen decided to turn toward the Antarctic instead and strike for the still-unconquered South Pole. He made his plans swiftly and secretly. When well under way southbound, he had a terse message relayed to Scott, then in New Zealand: "Heading south. Amundsen."

For all his personal ambitions and his aggressive methods of achieving them, Amundsen was a highly capable explorer. He had wintered-over in the Antarctic, led three expeditions into the Arctic. His experience in the far north began to pay off perfectly when, on October 19, 1911, he started for the South Pole from his Framheim base at the Bay of Whales, at the opposite side of the Ross Ice Shelf from Scott's winter camp at McMurdo Sound. For one thing, Amundsen realized that a small lack, in transport or in food, could spell disaster. So he operated with a plentiful surplus of both. Each of his four sledges was drawn by 13 Greenland Huskies. Unlike the British, Amundsen was an expert dog-team handler, well taught by Eskimos in the Arctic. He had established depots along the intended route. In long, hard ice-shelf practice runs he had trained his men and dogs to operate as close-knit teams.

THE final trip went off as smoothly as Peary's had on his assault on the North Pole. Amundsen and the four men with him rode the sledges for the first 100 miles, and for the next 300 were towed on their skis, thus completing about half of the polar trip without any heavy exertion at all. The next leg was the ascent of the mountain slopes. At the top the men killed all but 18 of the strongest dogs and cached the meat for return-trip rations. The party was still so fresh that when the men set off across the upper plateau they were able to travel some 20 miles a day.

On December 14, 1911, a bright, clear day, Amundsen triumphantly unfurled the flag of his country, Norway, at the South Pole, and named the high land around it King Haakon VII Plateau. He had one ironic

CHARLES WILKES (1798-1877), a U.S. naval officer, led the first American expedition to the Antarctic and was the first explorer to insist that Antarctica is a continent and not just endless fields of ice.

● In 1838, he sailed from Hampton Roads, Virginia, and reached the Weddell Sea, but storms coated his leaky ships with ice and scurvy broke out in the crews.

● In 1839, having wintered in Australia, he again attacked the ice belt. On January 30, 1840, still sailing through "forests of bergs," he believed he saw land and called it "the Antarctic Continent." The part he saw was named Wilkes Land by Mawson's party 72 years later.

● In 1842, after his return to America, Wilkes was court-martialed for cruelty to his men. He was acquitted, however, and went on to gain the rank of rear admiral.

assignment to complete. Knowing that his rival was not far behind, and that he would undoubtedly reach the pole too, he left a note for Scott, asking him to forward a letter to King Haakon.

The return journey was as close to being a lark as any polar trip could be. Halfway back, Amundsen jubilantly wrote in his diary, "We had such masses of biscuits that we could positively throw them about."

Amundsen's triumph is a bitter contrast to the journey of Robert F. Scott and his four companions, Dr. E. A. Wilson, Lieutenant Henry R. Bowers, Captain Lawrence E. C. Oates and Petty Officer Edgar Evans. Captain Scott did not share Amundsen's faith in dogs as motive power. As in earlier explorations, he relied on man power for moving sledges, supported for the first leg of the journey by Siberian ponies. Even during the preparation at his winter quarters, he wondered if his decision about the ponies was wise. They began to suffer from skin parasites, and they needed careful protection from the cold and wind. Scott wrote, "I am afraid there is much pony trouble in store. . . ."

Scott's luck was terrible. During October, 1911, as the time to head south drew near, the animals went off their feed, several of the men suffered illness or accident, and unseasonable storms raged. The weather, Scott noted, was "wretched." His party was still a week from being ready to depart when, on the 23rd of October, he heard of Amundsen's start from the Bay of Whales on the other side of the Ross Sea.

"I don't know what to think of Amundsen's chances," wrote Scott. "If he gets to the Pole, it must be before we do, as he is bound to travel fast with dogs. . . . I decided at a very early date to act exactly as I should have done had he not existed. Any attempt to race must have wrecked my plan, besides which it doesn't appear the sort of thing one is out for . . . you must be prepared," he concluded, "for the chance of finding our venture much belittled."

WEDNESDAY, November 1, Scott headed inland, and next day reached Hut Point, above McMurdo Sound and the real point of take-off for his thrust into the interior. "We shall start in three parties," he wrote, adding soon afterward that "we have decided to begin night marching." Scott's route was due south across the ice shelf, and then up the approximately 110-mile-long Beardmore Glacier to the 8,000-foot-high plateau across which the final 350-mile dash to the pole would be made. The ponies were to transport the supplies to the foot of the glacier. All the rest of the way to the pole and back to the coast—a total distance of about 1,800 miles —the sledges and supplies were to be manhandled. It was a closely calculated plan, and test runs from the winter base and Scott's own earlier trips over the inland ice sheet showed it could work.

But there was nothing Scott could do about the elements. The ice surfaces turned out to be treacherous, the winds fierce, the weather dreadful. For four critical days the party was stopped in its tracks less than 400 miles from the coast by a tremendous blizzard. Wrote Scott: "Sunday, December 3—Camp 29. Our luck in weather is preposterous." "December 5—A raging, howling blizzard. . . . What on earth does such weather mean at this time of year?"

It was not until December 9 that the expedition was able to continue. Mounds of fresh snow lay on the trail, and it was heavy going up the

SIR JAMES CLARK ROSS (1800-1862), British rear admiral, made the greatest antarctic voyages of the 19th Century. He was first to penetrate the ice pack into the Ross Sea and discovered the Ross Ice Shelf, where most 20th Century explorers have made their base camps.

● He blundered onto the ice shelf during his first voyage in 1841 while trying to sail to the South Magnetic Pole.

● He also surveyed 500 miles of coast, calling it Victoria Land, and discovered twin volcanoes which he named after his ships, the "Erebus" and "Terror."

● He returned to the Ross Sea in 1841 and his ships were nearly sunk when they collided in a gale amid icebergs. On his last expedition in 1842 he failed to reach a record penetration of the Weddell Sea but surveyed parts of Graham Land.

furrowed glacier, pulling the 350-pound, loaded sledges in harness. But the men had to rely on their own legs; it was their theory that human will power was the most important asset. Straining, the eight remaining men topped the glacier and moved out at last onto the polar plateau. Then, 150 miles from the pole, Scott sent the last support team back. Five men would make up the "Pole party." The leader took out a new notebook and wrote on the flyleaf on December 22: "Ages: Self 43, Wilson 39, Evans (P.O.) 37, Oates 32, Bowers 28. Average 36."

It was antarctic midsummer. They were at Camp 44, at an altitude of 7,100 feet, with the temperature 1° below zero. The situation looked bright when "with 7 hours' marching we covered 10½ miles," so much so that Scott was able to add, "tomorrow we march longer hours, about 9 I hope. Every day the loads will lighten and so we ought to make the requisite progress." But on January 8, 1912, the diary recorded "our first summit blizzard." Two days later they experienced a "terrible hard march in the morning." They were by then some 85 miles from the pole, but making poor progress on the difficult surface. Now the effects of having no animals to pull the sledge were beginning to tell. "The rest of the forenoon was agonizing," wrote Scott on the 11th. "I never had such pulling; all the time the sledge rasps and creaks. We have covered 6 miles, but at fearful cost to ourselves."

January 12: "Only 63 miles from the Pole."

January 14: ". . . less than 40 miles from the Pole. . . . Oh! for a few fine days! So close it seems and only the weather to baulk us."

January 15: "Only 27 miles from the Pole. We ought to do it now."

The mile-by-mile struggle, the ordeal by storm and hunger and frostbite—these were as nothing compared to the shock recorded in Scott's entry on January 16: "The worst has happened, or nearly the worst. We marched well in the morning and covered 7½ miles. Noon sight showed us in Lat. 89° 42′ S., and we started off in high spirits in the afternoon, feeling that tomorrow would see us at our destination. About the second hour of the march Bowers' sharp eyes detected what he thought was a cairn. . . . We marched on, found that it was a black flag tied to a sledge bearer; near by the remains of a camp; sledge tracks and ski tracks going and coming and the clear trace of dogs' paws—many dogs. This told us the whole story." It was one of Amundsen's camps.

On the 18th, Scott found Amundsen's South Pole tent, with the record that the five Norwegians had been there. He also found Amundsen's note: "Asks me to forward a letter to King Haakon!" Then: "Well, we have turned our back now on the goal of our ambition and must face our 800 miles of solid dragging—and good-bye to most of the day-dreams!"

As the Scott party started back, their food rations were low. They had established depots along the route, and the diary becomes a harrowing account, during the next two months, of struggling from one cache to another for the food to keep going.

Coming back down the glacier from the summit, Evans took a bad fall. Their pace slowed. On February 7, Scott recorded his "First panic." One of the biscuit boxes was found to have a shortage—amounting to a full day's rations for the men. They were so close to starvation now that a single ration box was a vital matter.

SIR DOUGLAS MAWSON (1882-1958), Australian geologist, made many important geographic and scientific discoveries in the Antarctic. One of the Shackleton party that found the South Magnetic Pole in 1909, he returned twice with expeditions of his own.

● In 1911, he began a three-year survey of the coast between King George V Land and Queen Mary Land, a distance of 1,500 miles. His charts united the earlier discoveries of Scott, Wilkes and d'Urville.

● In 1912, his expedition suffered a double tragedy. One of Mawson's companions fell into a crevasse and was lost; the other died of food poisoning. Mawson staggered on alone 165 miles to his ship.

● In 1929, during further explorations, he studied wildlife and pioneered the use of aircraft and radio on antarctic trips.

By mid-February, Evans showed signs of mental breakdown. On the 17th he collapsed, fell into a coma and died. "Providence to our aid!" wrote Scott. "We can expect little from man now. . . ." Oates began to suffer from frostbite as the temperatures went lower, day by day. He suffered intense pain for three weeks. One morning he asked the others what they thought he should do. "Nothing could be said," wrote Scott, "but to urge him to march as long as he could." On March 17 a blizzard blew. As the men huddled in their tent, Oates pulled himself heavily to his feet and said: "I am just going outside and may be some time." With that, the stalwart Guards officer hobbled off into the whiteness. He was never seen again.

"It was the act of a brave man and an English gentleman," wrote Scott. But it was already too late. The three survivors were so badly frostbitten they could hardly move. "Amputation is the least I can hope for," wrote Scott on March 19. "The weather doesn't give us a chance."

DAY by day the marches had been getting shorter, until four and a half miles was as far as the men could move their sledge in a day. On the 21st, with just two days' rations left, and only 11 miles from a food depot, the terrible antarctic winter closed in. For a week the three men were imprisoned by a fierce blizzard and no entries were made in the diary. Then, on March 29, Scott wrote:

"Every day we have been ready to start for our depot 11 *miles* away, but outside the door of the tent it remains a scene of whirling drift. I do not think we can hope for any better things now. We shall stick it out to the end, but we are getting weaker, of course, and the end cannot be far. It seems a pity, but I do not think I can write more."

He signed his name: "R. Scott." The fading hand had strength for one last entry: "For God's sake, look after our people."

A search party found the tent and the bodies eight months later. Each man lay in his sleeping bag. Beneath Scott's arm were his diary and a few last letters. "Had we lived," wrote Scott in one letter, "I should have had a tale to tell of the hardihood, endurance and courage of my companions which would have stirred the heart of every Englishman." The diary of Captain Scott survives as his monument, one of the imperishable documents in the annals of exploration. Scott and his companions were no men to let polar tradition down. Even while struggling along and literally dying on their feet, they still carried with them 35 pounds of precious fossils and other geologic specimens collected en route to the South Pole— specimens which helped scientists determine the age and history of that part of the antarctic continent.

The great dream of *terra australis* really ended that antarctic summer of 1911-1912, with Amundsen's triumph and Scott's tragedy. Today men live and work in a station maintained by the United States at the pole where the drama of discovery was enacted half a century ago. The airplane, the snow tractor, an atomic power station and wireless communication have transformed the Antarctic as a scene of human endeavor. As the 1957-1958 International Geophysical Year so richly demonstrated, the Antarctic has become a scientific laboratory for many nations. Yet the new scientific searchers, probing its ice and measuring its winds, are the first to grant that most of their laboratory's secrets are still undisclosed.

ROALD AMUNDSEN (LEFT), FIRST AT THE SOUTH POLE, TAKES A SIGHTING AS THE FLAG OF HIS NATIVE NORWAY WHIPS IN THE WIND

Explorers of Antarctica

The superb skill—and the unusually fair weather—that attended Roald Amundsen's attainment of the South Pole made his feat look almost effortless. It was not. But there was more drama, if less glory, in the polar assaults made by many of those who followed him. Here is an album that shows some of the triumphs and disasters these men experienced in gaining an immortality of their own.

CAPTAIN ROBERT FALCON SCOTT, R.N., BEFORE HIS LAST EXPEDITION

Scott's Tragic Second Best

The great tragic chapter of antarctic history is provided by the 1911-1913 Scott expedition to the South Pole. Robert Scott had no faith in dog teams, a misplaced faith in ponies, and utter faith that his men could haul sledges on most of the round trip to the pole from the advance base, about 1,200 miles. Scott and four companions did reach the pole after a struggle—to find that Amundsen, using Eskimo dogs, had beaten them by a month. Discouraged at being second, Scott and his men turned back, but they never made it. One man died after a fall. Another, so frostbitten that he could hardly hobble, committed suicide by wandering out to freeze in a blizzard. Scott and his two remaining companions, pinned down by a storm, froze to death in their tent.

A SUPPORT PARTY uses Siberian ponies in a supply caravan
to depots set up along the route to the pole.
The ponies could not stand the cold and died off quickly.

SCOTT'S LAST BIRTHDAY is celebrated at McMurdo
Sound on June 6, 1911, as the men await
the antarctic summer. Scott is at the head of the table.

THE POLE PARTY hauls a sledge on the final, 350-mile trek.
Pulling 180 pounds each, they exhausted
the energy that might have saved them on the return trip.

SCOTT'S ORDEAL shows on his face as he stands, at
center, with the men he took to the pole. Bowers
(*seated, left*) pulled the string to take this grim portrait.

SCOTT'S PARTY finds the
Amundsen tent and flag at the
South Pole (*above*). Notes
inside the tent told Scott
how badly he had been beaten.

SCOTT'S GRAVE is marked
by a tall cairn and a cross (*below*)
erected by the rescue party
that found the bodies and saved
Scott's diary and photographs.

THE "ENDURANCE" TRAPPED is helpless in the pack ice of the Weddell Sea. Shackleton's party stayed aboard for 10 months while the ship drifted 573 miles with the ice.

THE "ENDURANCE" CRUSHED sinks slowly through the thick ice (*opposite*), its decks a confusion of tangled rigging and snapped masts, its hold full of ice and brine.

The Shackleton Odyssey

Sir Ernest Shackleton was the first man to con-
ceive of pushing an expedition clear across the
antarctic continent. He never succeeded, but his
two-year odyssey is perhaps the most extraordinary of all antarctic adventures. Hardly had
Shackleton's ship, the *Endurance*, entered the
Weddell Sea, where the first base was to be located, than it became locked in the ice (*opposite*).
Drifting inexorably toward the interior of the ice
pack, the ship's hull was slowly crushed (*below*),
and Shackleton and his 26 men had to camp on
the shifting, treacherous floes. Worse still, they
found they were unable to drag their supplies and
lifeboats either toward land or open water. Their
only chance was to try to stay alive on the ice.

Always cold and wet, living on a dull diet of
seal meat and in daily peril of being overwhelmed
by the giant floes, they did survive. At last the
pack drifted north to open water. They launched
their boats and reached bleak Elephant Island,
after a fearful voyage, on April 15, 1916. They
had last touched dry land on December 5, 1914.

SIR ERNEST SHACKLETON AT A CAMP ON THE ICE

MEN IN THE SURF launch a lifeboat from the beach
on Elephant Island. Every man knew that
if this boat foundered, all hope of rescue went with her.

Shackleton Gets Through

Once Shackleton had brought his men and boats to Elephant Island, he had to face an agonizing decision: how best to get help, for if he remained where he was, he and his entire party would starve to death. With characteristic vigor he decided at once to try to sail one of the lifeboats 800 miles to South Georgia Island, where he knew there was a Norwegian whaling station. He was at sea for 16 days in the stormiest waters in the world, drenched, frozen and starving, but he made it. Unfortunately he landed on the wrong side of South Georgia, and had to climb over a previously unscaled mountain range to reach the whaling station. Even then, it was months before a ship could get through the ice to rescue the men on Elephant Island. During this extraordinary saga, not one of Shackleton's men died.

MEN IN HARNESS strain to haul a lifeboat over the ice, trying to reach open water. After 18 men took a week to move two boats seven miles, they gave up and made camp.

THE MAROONED MEN stand on the desolate beach (*below*) as the rescue ship heaves into sight. After three months, their supplies were coming to an end.

Byrd and the Airplane

The first man to use the airplane in exploring the Antarctic was Admiral Richard E. Byrd. In 1929, eighteen years after Amundsen had toiled for 99 days to reach the South Pole and return to his base, Byrd flew his trimotored Fokker, the *Floyd Bennett*, 1,600 miles from Little America (*below*) to the pole and back in one day. Returning to Little America in 1933, Byrd almost died of monoxide poisoning when the stove malfunctioned in a weather hut (*right*) he was manning alone, 123 miles from the base. Otherwise this expedition and a third in 1939 went smoothly.

Using the newest aircraft, Byrd and his crews flew over vast reaches of the continent, mapping its coasts and mountain ranges. On the 1939 expedition alone they mapped 100,000 square miles of land. Byrd also commanded the Navy expedition of 1946-1947 and the great "Operation Deepfreeze" in 1956 which made massive use of the methods and equipment he had pioneered.

IN A WEATHER HUT, spending the winter of 1934 alone, Byrd cooks a meal. During his stay in the 9-by-12-foot hut, monoxide fumes from the stove almost killed him.

THE "FLOYD BENNETT" comes in for a landing at Little America, the base Byrd established in 1929. The steel radio towers were 65 feet tall.

ADMIRAL RICHARD E. BYRD, a stalwart 68 (*opposite*), is back for "Operation Deepfreeze" in 1956, his fifth and final antarctic expedition. He died in 1957.

68

Scott's Base, 50 Years Later

The base camp set up by Captain Scott in 1910-1911 before his fatal trip to the South Pole has withstood the winds and snows of more than 50 years. A lonely, weather-beaten shack at Cape Evans on McMurdo Sound (*opposite*), it stands in sad contrast to the elaborate and comfortable quarters provided for the men of the nearby U.S. naval air facility built in 1955-1956. When the remaining members of Scott's expedition left the camp 10 months after his death they abandoned food, supplies, sledges, a disabled tractor and other gear. It is all still there, preserved by the dryness of the air and the extreme cold, and protected now from the souvenir hunters of modern expeditions by being designated a British National Shrine.

PEMMICAN in cans rests
on the floor of Scott's hut
(*left*). It was found to be still
edible by the 1955-1956
expedition that explored the camp.

A MOTOR SLEDGE stands where Scott abandoned it.
Ski-mounted and powered for heavy hauling,
three such sledges proved useless after many breakdowns.

SCOTT'S DINING TABLE remains intact (*right*).
Last used in 1917 by later explorers,
the hut is strewn with sifted snow, but the walls look new.

SCOTT'S HUT stands half buried
in snow (*right*) facing
McMurdo Sound. Nearby stand
supplies and sledges left when
the survivors departed in 1913.

AGILE HIGH JUMPER, an Adélie penguin vaults aboard an ice floe. Using their webbed feet and vestigial wings, penguins can swim like porpoises and often leap seven feet straight up out of the water.

4

Rigors of Polar Life

EMPEROR penguins in the rookeries close by the American antarctic base at McMurdo Sound have been observed stolidly shielding their eggs in the teeth of a 90-mile-an-hour blizzard. Musk oxen on the west coast of Ellesmere Island, high in the Canadian Arctic, have been seen grazing placidly in 50°-below-zero cold. In such extremes, neither penguins nor musk oxen are in danger of freezing to death. Along with most other arctic and antarctic animals, they have an amazing capacity to function despite punishing cold and wind. The adaptations which make this possible are few and highly specialized. They relate to one of evolution's major developments: warm-bloodedness.

Wherever a homeothermic, or warm-blooded, animal goes it takes along its own private, internal climate. Whatever the weather outside (within limits, of course), its body basks in tropical heat, carefully maintained at close to 100° by a sensitive thermostat in the brain. Warm-bloodedness is an attribute of the higher forms of life, shared by all mammals and birds, including tropical ones, but its usefulness is most dramatic in the polar cold.

This intricate heat-control mechanism is relatively rare. There are about a million kinds of animals on earth and some 980,000 of them are cold-blooded, or poikilothermic. All of these—the reptiles, the fish and the insects, among many others—simply tend to take on the temperature of their surroundings; when it gets warm they are warm and active, and when it gets cold they are cold and torpid. A few of them can stay alive, though hardly functional, at fantastic depths of cold that would kill anything else, but almost all of them become inactive and helpless if the temperature merely drops to about 40° or rises to about 108°. So the cold-blooded creatures, except for fish and insects, must leave the polar regions to the warm-blooded ones. Fish survive because the salt water they live in never quite freezes, though it may get colder than 32°—and by polar standards the freezing point is warm. Some insects find refuge in the warm fur or feathers of homeotherms but most, like the Arctic's clouds of black flies and mosquitoes, come to life only on the few warm days of summer.

For the flexibility that enables the warm-blooded animal to make a living in climates far colder than its internal one, it pays a stiff price. Most of the food it eats has to be used in generating heat. For example, even when a man feels comfortably warm he is using over half his total calorie intake just to maintain his body temperature. The colder it gets outside the body, the more food he needs. He is so ill-equipped for intense cold that he soon reaches a state where he cannot stay warm no matter how much he eats. Stripped naked at zero he will freeze to death in a few minutes. In fact the critical exterior temperature for man—below which he cannot maintain his basal metabolism without losing body temperature—is about 80°. The foregoing applies to the white man and even among his race, the Caucasoid, there are individual differences in the toleration of heat and cold. Critical temperatures have not been established for all races and groups of people; certainly some aboriginal tribes show a remarkable capacity to withstand cold even when thinly clad. But all such human variations are no more than a difference in degree—or at most a few degrees.

Thus warm-bloodedness alone does not guarantee survival in the realms of cold. It does insure that its possessor will be alert and active as long as body heat is conserved. Man insulates his body with heavy clothing and shelter. Some animals are insulated with fur, fat or feathers, and take shelter too. Some hibernate in coldest winter, and others migrate to avoid it. Most striking of all the adaptations are those internal physiological processes which help conserve, tolerate and dissipate heat.

The idea that warm-blooded animals of the same or related species tend to be larger in cold regions and to become smaller toward the equator was accepted for a long time. The principle, called Bergmann's rule, had sound physics behind it—the larger an object, the more slowly it tends to lose heat. The arctic fox is larger than the desert fox, the wood bison of central Canada is bigger than the buffalo of the American plains, and with some other species it seemed to be the same way. As a corollary it was assumed that the polar varieties tended to have shorter appendages—and some do—because a long nose and tail, long ears and legs add unnecessarily to the body surface and are great heat wasters. The trouble with such rules was that there were too many exceptions to them. Polar animals did not all tend to globular, woolly shapes with stubby appendages, and tropical species did not all tend to skinny shapes with long appendages.

More recently scientists have realized that the animals' primary heat-preserving mechanism is not size or shape but insulation. It takes two forms: a layer of fat, or of tissue heavily impregnated with oil, just under the skin; and a layer of fur or feathers just over the skin. Thus insulated, the penguin can frolic for hours in near-freezing water which would quickly kill a man. Some animals' insulation is almost too efficient. Long ago, explorers found that European dogs such as German shepherds were useless on polar trips because they were too lightly furred. The sledge dog, such as the Alaskan Malemute or the Siberian Husky, has a much thicker pelt; on cold winter nights it sleeps most comfortably when snow drifts over its body and shelters it from the wind.

Just as a bird ruffles its feathers, a dog or wolf or fox can fluff out its fur to trap air and gain temporary warmth. It can reduce heat loss by modifying its shape, curling up in a ball to rest or sleep with nose and ears, paws and tail all tucked in. For better winter insulation the musk ox grows its inner matting of fine, long quviut every fall; by the time the temperatures drop and the winds rise, the animal is so effectively double-blanketed that the snow does not melt where an ox lies down. But the lighter-colored coats that the fox and the weasel, for instance, adopt for winter are for camouflage, not for better heat-conserving. In the dark arctic winter the rays received by the animals' fur and reflected from it are infrared and invisible; their heat penetrates one shade of fur as well as another.

The fur bearers need efficient ways of getting rid of heat as well as ways of hoarding it. The caribou that is peacefully grazing one moment may have to try to outrun a wolf the next, and the heat production of both may be increased twentyfold in the chase. This is when their thin belly fur and thin-skinned ears, legs and tail—and panting tongue, too—serve them well, predator and prey alike.

THE EARS OF FOXES help radiate body heat, and so diminish in size in three species living in progressively colder climates. The kit fox of the deserts of the American Southwest, at bottom, has the largest ears. The red fox of the fields and forests of the eastern U.S. has ears of intermediate size and, to conserve body heat, the arctic fox has the smallest ears.

Mᴏʀᴇ noteworthy than their tolerance of cold is the fact that many polar animals can also stand extreme heat. It is during the relatively hot weather that carbohydrates in the food are converted into fat, for winter insulation and nourishment. Experimenters at the Arctic Research Laboratory at Point Barrow found that the abundant ground squirrel (called *sic-sic* by the Eskimos) of the arctic slope, along with polar bear cubs, weasels, foxes and dogs, could endure temperatures 10° C. higher than such desert denizens as the pack rat and kangaroo rat. Evidently the same precise controls that regulate metabolism and circulation to cope with cold may also be effective against heat.

There is nothing particularly surprising about the animals' use of fur, fat and feathers for insulation. Less apparent, and less widely understood, is the strange ability of some animals to maintain *two* internal temperatures, a tropical one for the body in general and a radically lower one for the extremities. Laurence Irving of the Arctic Health Research Center in Anchorage has found that the sea gull's feet may be kept at 32°, nearly 70° colder than the rest of its body. Some arctic birds prevent their legs and feet from freezing by stepping up the blood circulation to the legs while still keeping them much colder than the body. The nervous systems of these cold-tolerant birds function at low temperatures where warm-climate birds would be immobilized.

The leg temperatures of reindeer, Husky dogs and some other arctic mammals have shown readings about 50° lower than their bodies. The thin flukes and flippers of seals and subarctic porpoises are kept not at body temperature, but almost as low as the water temperature. In many of these species a simple but effective heat-exchange apparatus does the trick. The arteries bearing warm blood toward the extremities are closely bunched or entwined with the veins carrying cold blood back to the heart. The warm blood is cooled, the cold blood is heated and the extremities are kept cold, so that they lose little heat.

A FEATHERED DANDY, the beplumed macaroni penguin gets its name from the overdressed gentlemen, or "macaronies," of the 18th Century lampooned in the song "Yankee Doodle." The bird nests on beaches of the subantarctic islands.

A RAUCOUS TYPE, the Magellanic penguin is often called the jackass penguin because of its braying call. It is native to the southern tip of South America, especially the islands in the Strait of Magellan, from which it receives its name.

THE TIMID GENTOO, or Johnny penguin, is the commonest of all the varieties. Living on subantarctic islands and accustomed to having to flee marine enemies, the Gentoo will waddle inland when approached on the beach by a man or a dog.

THIS remarkable double standard of internal heating almost seems a step in the direction of cold-bloodedness—or in the direction of the animals that hibernate while their temperature, breathing and metabolism all decline. It is not easy to hibernate in the polar regions. The rodents cannot dig beneath the frost line. The lemmings, shrews, voles and weasels escape the cold by digging burrows in the snow. Next to the ground, at the bottom of the snow cover, it seldom is colder than 20° and within the burrows it is usually warmer. The inhabitants have no need of hibernation. Safe from the predators that are on the prowl in the open air above, and with a snow-buried supply of plants only a nibble away, their lives are secure —until the thaw melts their snow ramparts and their burrows crumble on the ground. Meanwhile the ground squirrels, the marmots and some bigger mammals, up to the barren-ground grizzlies, curl up or den up and all but suspend life for the winter, while their body temperatures may drop nearly to freezing. Until the weather warms, they get nourishment from their accumulated fat. The insulating snow protects them from the worst of the cold, and hibernation relieves them of having to go out and find food in the dead of winter.

Other polar creatures, from caribou (and the wolves and wolverines that dog their trail) to ducks, protect themselves from the winter cold by migrating. Birds are the proverbial migrants of this world, and when winter comes to the top of the world flocks of waterfowl leave. Even the snow bunting, the only songbird of the tundra, flies south. The world's champion traveler is the arctic tern, the only species with homes in both polar regions. Every autumn it takes off and flies 8,000 to 10,000 miles down to the Antarctic—almost halfway around the world—to find the icy open waters it likes. Then at the change of season it flies all the way back. Seven months of the year the tern is on the wing; it returns to its native rookery only for the nesting season. The jaeger is a year-round predator: in summer it preys on other birds and lemmings on the tundra; in winter it migrates east or west to the sea and as far as South Africa to hunt for fish. It often chases feeding gulls and makes them drop what they have caught. The golden plover is one of the Arctic's greatest navigators: three months after it arrives in the world as an egg, it can fly well enough to take off with its elders from the Alaskan beaches on an unerring, nonstop two-day flight to the Hawaiian Islands.

Despite their ingenious and near-perfect defenses against heat loss, all warm-blooded animals must lose some heat. With every breath, they take in cold air which must be warmed before it comes in contact with delicate lung tissue; they often eat cold food or drink cold water which must be warmed to body temperature; they lose heat with the warmth of feces and urine. None of their insulating defenses is complete. They need energy—and expend heat—for swimming, running or flying, and for the building and replacement of body tissue. They may live and even thrive in the coldest of climates—only so long as the food supply is ample.

Like all animal life, the polar animals must get their food from the green plants. Of all living things, only the green plants can carry on the life-giving process of photosynthesis, which converts the radiant energy of the sun into food. To get this energy every animal must eat the green plants, or eat other animals that do.

For proper growth the plants need sunlight and air, water and certain minerals. If any one of these is missing, the plant cannot manufacture food for itself or for anything else. In large areas around the poles, one or more of these raw materials is in short supply. But these shortages are no more critical in the lives of the plants than is the cold. For plants, much in the manner of the cold-blooded animals, take on the temperature of their environment, and the complex chemistry of photosynthesis and growth, like all chemical processes, seems to slow down as the thermometer goes down. Even the simplest plants of the polar regions must have a few days each year when the temperature is above 32°, and the more complicated plants need several weeks of frost-free weather to survive.

The Antarctic knows no such luxury as frost-free weeks. On the little ice-free edging along some of the continent's shores—perhaps 1,000 square miles of bare land—the air temperature goes above freezing no more than 20 days a year. (On the sparse soil and on the sun-warmed rocks, it gets a little warmer.) Mineral nutrients are few and the earth is poor in nitrogen. Virtually all the nitrogen that plants get originates in the air. Few plants can extract it directly. Most depend on lightning in the sky or bacteria in the soil to convert the nitrogen into usable form—and in the polar regions both lightning and soil bacteria are rare. The richest ground is at the penguin rookeries, where the droppings and decaying bodies of penguins build up nitrogen for thousands of years—but any plant that takes root there is doomed to be pecked to pieces by the birds.

ONE essential the plants do not lack at either pole is light. Weak as the sunlight is when it strikes the earth at a slant, it compares well enough with the light at lower latitudes, or at least is sufficient for plant growth, since even the most efficient green plants can use only about 5 per cent of the light that falls on them. Wherever dense stands of plants do take hold in the polar regions, their rate of growth and food-productivity in the growing season is a match for that of lower-latitude plants. The growing season is the catch: it is so short and uncertain that the land's total yield is low.

All this being so, the most successful plants in the Antarctic are the simplest ones, the algae and lichens and mosses. Over 150 species of algae do grow; given a halfway favorable place to start, the tiny plants will often daub a drab slope with green. The lichen is supreme in the antarctic flora. Actually it is not one plant but two, an alga which carries on photosynthesis and a fungus which cannot. The fungus plays a multiple role: it anchors the feeble algae cells to the rocks, and its fibers hold moisture, which gives the algae a better water supply than if they lived alone. Some lichen fungi may also secrete a substance that dissolves the rock, releasing minerals the lichen needs for growth. At all events, the lichens develop with incredible slowness. They may have just one day a year of active growth,

A VORACIOUS PIRATE, the skua raids penguin rookeries, killing hundreds of chicks but eating only eyes and kidneys. It also preys on other skuas and even eats its own fledglings. Its wingspread is up to four and a half feet.

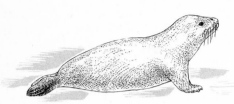

THE CRABEATER SEAL of the Antarctic has curiously cusped back teeth which intermesh to form a fine sieve. The seal gulps a mouthful of sea water and then spurts it out through the teeth, trapping the rich zooplankton the water contains.

THE SOUTHERNMOST MAMMAL is the Weddell seal; it sticks close to the antarctic continent while the other southern seals range far to sea. It chews breathing holes in the offshore ice and rests in natural chambers in the piled-up floes.

A VICIOUS CARNIVORE, the sleek leopard seal preys on other antarctic seal species and is the chief marine enemy of the penguin. Its large size—10 to 12 feet —deep jaw and sharp teeth all contribute to its deadly efficiency as a hunter.

and it is possible that antarctic lichens five inches across may be the earth's oldest living things. Their tenacity is terrific: lichens kept 15 years in museum cases have revived when watered.

The mosses, not quite so sturdy, may grow only after lichen bodies have formed a thin soil. But they are hardy enough; often in the dead of winter mosses will get so dry and brittle that they crumble to the touch. Yet at the first sign of warmth and moisture they assume the delicate and life-bearing texture of growing plants.

In the entire Antarctic there are only two flowering plants and both of them—one a species of grass, the other a relative of the carnation—live on the Palmer Peninsula, which has the region's mildest climate. Scientists suspect that they are recent arrivals, perhaps from South America.

Such a poverty-stricken flora could hardly nourish any sizable animal population, and Antarctica's does not. Yet thousands of sea birds, penguins, seals and whales crowd its cold coasts. It is no contradiction, for the animals are not oriented to the land but rather to the sea, and the antarctic waters have possibly the richest plant life in the world.

SURROUNDING the continent from 300 to 1,200 miles offshore is a strip of water averaging 28 miles in width. This band of water is the so-called Antarctic Convergence, the region within the sea where relatively warm water flowing south encounters the colder mass of northward-flowing antarctic water. The warm water contains dissolved mineral salts; the cold water has a lower mineral content, since it is diluted by melting ice, but is higher in oxygen. Where they join there is a well-nourished expanse of tiny plants, the phytoplankton. Their chlorophyll often stains the water of the convergence bright green, and a bucket of water hauled up on deck will smell like new-mown grass.

Feeding on these green pastures is an enormous swarm of drifting speck-sized marine animals called zooplankton. Larger creatures—tiny crabs, tiny fish—devour the zooplankton by the billions and in turn are eaten by still larger feeders, the big fish and squids of the open sea. Seals, penguins and gulls eat the fish and squids, and at the end of the omnivorous life chain come the large predators. The biggest of these is the killer whale, which consumes penguins and seals and even smaller whales; the stomach of one killer contained 13 porpoises and 14 seals. Another destroyer is the leopard seal, rapacious rogue of the peaceable seal family, eater of penguins and fellow seals. On shore a flying marauder, the giant skua, preys on penguin chicks and other birds.

Despite all the depredations of the predators, the populations of antarctic birds and animals are relatively large, which underscores a basic fact of polar life. In such rigorous environments there is a paucity of species of plants and animals—yet each tends to be represented by many individuals. Quite the contrary situation prevails in warmer areas where there are many species, tending to fewer members. Superficially it almost seems as if nature has been able to evolve only a few designs that would function well in the more difficult parts of the world; but once these designs were perfected they were, so to say, put into mass production. Actually, many other species simply could not adjust to the cold and were wiped out in the ice ages. The polar regions as a result have "young" flora and fauna; they are still recovering from the disaster.

In the entire region south of the Antarctic Circle, for example, there are fewer than 70 species of animals. Forty-four of these are insects, of which the largest is a wingless mosquito. This is an astonishingly small insect population for such a vast area, considering that nine out of 10 of all the world's animal species are insects. There are no land mammals at all in Antarctica and only five kinds of seals inhabit the waters around the continent. Possibly the most imposing population in the far south is made up of birds, but even these occur in notably small variety. Less than a dozen in all visit the continent, and then only briefly to breed. These include the South Polar skua, two petrels, the silver-gray fulmar, the Cape pigeon and two kinds of penguins. The other 16 species of penguins live in somewhat milder climates to the north.

All of the penguin species have the same basic design: a streamlined body formally attired in stubby black and white feathers. The front appendages of the bird have evolved into swimming flippers covered with feathers that are almost scalelike.

Some zoologists think that the penguin developed from some flying bird, and that the flippers represent modified wings. Others believe that because of the scaly flippers the strange bird may have descended from some non-flying reptilian ancestor. With its sleek body protected by plenty of fat under the skin, the penguin is well prepared to spend time in the sea. Except for the periods when it comes up on land or ice to molt and to rear its young, it is almost as aquatic as the porpoise. The Adélie penguin, most numerous of the species, spends the whole winter out on the ice, feeding on fish and squid and avoiding the predators. To get away from a leopard seal or a killer whale it can propel itself seven feet straight up out of the water to the safety of an ice floe.

As spring comes the Adélie waddles over the ice pack to the land's edge to breed. The bird fashions its nest out of pebbles—there is not much else available—and one of the traits that has endeared it to explorers is its use of the pebbles in its courtship. The male will solemnly present the female with a pebble, usually one it has stolen from another penguin's nest. This has its humorous side but the pilfering of rocks is really a matter of life and death for the penguin young, since an adequate nest for the parent to stand on is all that keeps the delicate egg above the level of the cold melt-water on the ground under the adult's body. Adélies will stay on their nests for the weeks of incubation, through fair weather and foul. Occasionally a whole rookery will be blotted out by a blizzard. The penguins do not move from their posts, but stay put in the snow, refusing to abandon their eggs until almost buried alive. During all the time that the eggs are being hatched, the parent on guard—sometimes the male, at other times the female—goes without food, living on its fat against the time when it can go back to sea to fatten up again on fish.

THE intermediate links in the long antarctic food chain are often bypassed by the whales. One large group, the baleen whales, which have no true teeth, feed directly on plankton, straining it out of the sea water with a bony sieve hanging from the roof of the mouth. The full-grown blue whale, at 150 tons the most monstrous creature that ever lived, eats its way through three tons of krill, a two-inch, shrimplike crustacean, every 24 hours. In all the seas, the only fishing of comparable scope is man's

THE ALASKA FUR SEAL, most magnificently coated of all, is the chief source of the pelts which are used in making sealskin coats. Furriers trim off an outer layer of coarse guard hair, revealing the thick, soft, fur plush next to the skin.

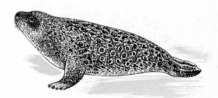

THE NORTHERNMOST MAMMAL is the ringed seal, living almost exclusively on or under the ice of the Arctic Ocean, seldom if ever venturing farther south. The white circles surrounding the patches of black in its fur give the animal its name.

THE HARP SEAL, commercially valuable for leather and oil, is hunted all over the Arctic. More than 500,000 animals are taken each year, largely by Russian sealers. The species takes its name from the black marking on the back of the adult.

own pursuit of the fish and whales. Much of the northern whale population having been slaughtered long ago, the Antarctic is now the center of the world whaling industry, which kills about 35,000 animals a year for food, fertilizer and industrial oils. The hunting is covered by international treaty, but still goes on at such a rate that the whales are dwindling.

In the Arctic, remnants of a half-dozen whale species survive, notably the 12-to-14-foot white whale and the long-tusked narwhal, both hunted by the Eskimos. Whales were never so numerous in the north, possibly because the Arctic Ocean is only intermittently paved with plankton. Much of its surface is covered by ice most of the year, reducing the amount of sunlight that can penetrate the water to nourish the plants. But if the Arctic Ocean has no life-giving phenomenon comparable to the Antarctic Convergence, it has a geophysical feature much vaster in size, though with influences on plant and animal life that are yet to be fully explored. This is the recently found Lomonosov ridge, a giant undersea wrinkle that runs 900 miles from the Asian continental shelf, past the neighborhood of the North Pole to the North American continental shelf, near Ellesmere Island. It rears up 6,000 to 11,000 feet from the bottom of the ocean basins and to within 3,200 feet of the surface, dividing the arctic deeps like a wall. According to its Soviet discoverers the ridge "plays a decisive role in determining the circulation and exchange of water among the different parts of the ocean, in setting the pattern of the ice drift, and in establishing the major provinces of life in the Arctic waters." But just how it does this awaits years of inquiry.

O F the warm-blooded species that have returned to the sea to escape enemies or find more ample food, the pinnipeds—fin-footed mammals— are by far the most prolific, probably the world's biggest population of big carnivorous animals. There are three families of them. The eared seals, including sea lions and fur seals, most closely resemble land mammals. They and the walruses (from the Swedish *hvalross*, which means "whale horse") have back flippers which can be used for "walking" on ice or land. In the third family are the earless, or true, seals, sometimes known as hair seals and including all the pinnipeds which dwell in the Antarctic. Their flippers are bent backward for better swimming, so they move awkwardly when out of water.

All these animals are magnificently insulated against polar chill, not by their sleek coats of hair—which are cold comfort when wet—but by their thick layers of fat.

Five of the 47 species of seals live in southern waters. The crabeater, the leopard and the rare Ross's seal spend their lives out at the edge of the ice pack. The Weddell seal prefers a life closer to shore. In winter, when its home waters are iced over, it keeps open a series of breathing holes which it chews through the ice from below. All winter long it swims from hole to hole, chomping through the new ice crusts that form. Biggest of all seals— up to 8,000 pounds—is the elephant seal, which breeds on subantarctic islands and goes south to feeding grounds all around the ice pack. The antarctic seals all bear their young in the spring, usually in September or October. The pups are born large and soon learn to live without their mothers. The Weddell seal pup, 60 pounds at birth, doubles its weight in two weeks on a straight diet of milk rated at 40 per cent butterfat.

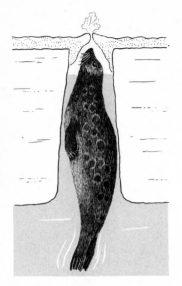

A CHIMNEY is chewed in the ice by a ringed seal. A series of such passages is kept open for breathing holes and for exits onto the ice. Seals surface for air every seven to nine minutes, but in an emergency can submerge for 20 minutes.

The whales and the seals of the Antarctic all have their relatives in the north. One is the walrus, a huge, strong and streamlined diver that plunges as deep as 200 feet to root out shellfish with its two-foot tusks. The Eskimo traditionally hunted the walrus for its meat, its fat and its ivory tusks, and in a primitive culture which had little or no metal the ivory was one of the few materials that could be worked for tools. The white men valued the ivory too, for ornamental uses. In 200 years of slaughter, the walrus was reduced from perhaps half a million animals to the present population of about 70,000. Today the most important species of the ubiquitous pinnipeds is the northern fur seal, whose only breeding ground is the Pribilof Islands in the Bering Sea. Most of the pelts for sealskin coats come from this prized animal, now rigorously protected by international law after being hunted almost to extinction. It has a counterpart in the subantarctic, the New Zealand fur seal, which also produces a fine fur pelt and is gaining in numbers under protection of the New Zealand government after being all but wiped out by fur hunters.

AN implacable enemy of the Arctic seals is the formidable polar bear. It is without any exception the most familiar of the polar creatures—almost any child can draw one—but its life cycle was long something of a mystery. Polar bears are tireless swimmers, gaining buoyancy from their fat and their dense coats of oily fur, and have been seen paddling away 25 miles from the nearest land. Just as the penguin would seem to be the antarctic animal most likely to succeed in the Arctic Ocean (where there are none), the polar bear would appear to be the one animal that would stand the best chance of surviving a transplant to the far south. It is to be seen wherever three things are found together in the Arctic: cold water, sea food and pack ice. If any one of the three is missing, so is the bear. Besides seals, the polar bear eats young walruses, fish, stranded dead whales, birds' eggs, and some seaweed. Occasionally it may abandon the ice, go a short distance inland and, like any bear, eat berries, grasses and rodents.

A pregnant female bear becomes dormant in a cave on the ice, giving birth to its cubs—usually two every second year—in midwinter. The cubs of a 700-pound mother weigh only two pounds at the most at birth and, depending on how the hunting goes on the ice, may or may not ever set foot on land during their lives.

The only carnivorous land animal that roams as far north as the polar bear is the arctic fox, which trails the bear—as the jackal trails the lion—for scraps of meat and sometimes, in desperation, has to exist on the bear's droppings. Eskimos used to trail the big bears with dogs and spears, but it was hazardous hunting until the Eskimos acquired rifles. Vilhjalmur Stefansson ate polar bear when he lived for five years on the ice of the northernmost Canadian islands 45 years ago. But strangers to the Arctic are warned not to eat the bear's liver, which is so rich in vitamin A that it may be highly toxic.

The southern limit of the polar bear's immense range is the edge of the drift ice. As for the northern limit, the first thing the lookout on the nuclear submarine *Skate* saw when his vessel surfaced near the North Pole was a polar bear ambling along nearby.

Unlike the Antarctic, the Arctic has vast stretches of ice-free land where animals can roam and plants can grow. There are immense regions of bare

A DEEP DIGGER for clams, the arctic walrus dredges shellfish from the sea bottom with its tusks. Sweeping the mollusks into its mouth with its stiff whiskers, it crushes the shells in strong jaws, spits them out and swallows the clams.

rock and of sterile gravel—but even larger regions covered by a thin mantle of soil formed from weathered rock and the slowly decaying remains of dead plants and animals. And although the Arctic receives scant precipitation, what little does fall is frozen into the soil as ice or collects in the numerous arctic lakes. Very little evaporates. When the sun warms the land, the ice at the soil surface melts and is suddenly available to the thirsting roots of the plants.

Sunlight needed for plant growth falls on the Arctic in abundance. As in the Antarctic, there are six months when the sun never sets. During the short arctic summer, plants are able to grow almost continuously. The few pollinating insects, including a bumblebee that lives as far north as the Peary Land section of Greenland, buzz tirelessly over them.

So complete is the adaptation of some arctic plants to long days that when they are taken south they do not seem to get enough light, and will not flower where there are long nights during the growing season. Such plants requiring long periods of light are fittingly called "long-day" plants. By contrast, many flowers in the middle latitudes are "short-day" plants and if grown under glass in the north they will grow into great, spindly giants. Many plants are not so finicky about the amount of light they receive. Some, like the cucumber, will grow healthily as long as there is sun. Cucumbers have grown five feet long in northern greenhouses.

THE most obvious hazard for arctic plants, as for those in the south polar region, is the combination of cold and a short growing season. Over extensive areas of the far north, it is too frigid for any plants except lichens, mosses and algae. These generally grow more abundantly than species in the Antarctic, and one arctic lichen, the so-called reindeer moss, grows six inches tall and is so widespread it furnishes pasturage for caribou, musk oxen and many other animals.

The flowering plants take hold in the Arctic only where the climate is mild enough to provide a few weeks of weather each year when the day and night temperatures stand above freezing. Like the animals, the arctic land plants have evolved all sorts of ways to conserve what heat they get. Many of them grow close to the soil in dense clumps or mats. This not only keeps the plants down out of the cold wind, but also lets them hug the soil which holds the warmth of the sun.

Because of the erratic growing season, which may bring a freezing day in the middle of summer, the plants that survive best in the Arctic are perennials, which means that they live for many years and attempt to produce flowers and seed each summer. If they fail, they can endure for several years without blossoming. Thus one bad growing season cannot wipe out the species. A great number of arctic plants have given up for good the uncertain method of reproducing by flower and seed. They propagate by sending out robust runners or underground shoots and bulbs. What appears to be a cluster of plants is often one parent plant surrounded by its offspring.

Linked to the plant growth of the Arctic is its own well-developed chain of land-animal life. Vegetarian species such as the lemming, the arctic hare, the caribou and the musk ox live prosperously off the plants. Preying on them are such carnivores as the weasels, the snowy owls, the foxes and the wolves. This contentious association of plants and animals makes up one of the world's great environmental units, known as the tundra.

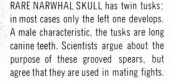

RARE NARWHAL SKULL has twin tusks; in most cases only the left one develops. A male characteristic, the tusks are long canine teeth. Scientists argue about the purpose of these grooved spears, but agree that they are used in mating fights.

AN INTRUDING SEA ELEPHANT SUNS ITSELF IN THE MIDST OF A GROUP OF RINGED PENGUINS ON THE COAST OF SOUTH GEORGIA

The Odd Polar Animals

The Arctic and Antarctic, which are hostile to most kinds of life, are hospitable to a few. The seas and shores support sizable populations of warm-blooded animals. Many of these creatures are odd—flightless birds, mammals that swim like fish, aquatic beasts that crawl on land. Some are vicious, some gentle, some amusing, and each has its own special ways to survive in the bitter polar cold.

83

ON THE ICE, penguins crowd a rookery off the coast of Adélie Land. In April about 14,000 emperors are camped on this stretch of ice, one of Antarctica's larger breeding grounds.

IN A HUDDLE, penguins pool their body heat when the antarctic winter deepens (*right*). Shoulders pressed together, they can weather 90-mile winds and 60°-below temperatures.

IN A PANIC, penguins toboggan at top speed to flee the noisy monster bearing down on them. The helicopter was taking part in the 1958 survey of Antarctica's penguin population.

The Perky, Peculiar Penguins

That curious, flightless bird, the penguin, lives only in the Southern Hemisphere. Most of the 18 species dwell either on far-south islands or on the edges of the southern continents—Australia, South America, Africa—although the Galápagos penguin has wandered up to the equatorial islands for which it is named. Only two, the tiny Adélie and the over-three-foot-tall emperor on these pages, are true dwellers of the Antarctic.

Nobody is sure where penguins originated or whether they ever flew, although it has been discovered from fossil remains that a five-foot penguin weighing about 250 pounds once wandered Antarctica. Penguins make wonderful use of their truncated wings to porpoise about in the water at up to 30 miles an hour. All species, though their head markings differ, have almost identical plumage—the well-known white shirt fronts, with backs and wings of rich black or midnight blue.

The Emperor's Domestic Life

The largest of all penguins, the emperor, has adopted as rigorous a regime for raising its young as any animal in the world. After a short summer of swimming off the antarctic coasts, emperors emerge from the sea in March, just as the antarctic autumn begins. Waddling or tobogganing on their stiffly feathered fronts, they head across what may be many miles of ice and somehow locate the same rookery they have used every year of their lives. There they congregate in colonies of up to 50,000 birds, and the males and females begin to pair off. Sometimes two females select the same male and this leads to short pitched battles (*left*).

Once male and female have reached agreement, they do not part until the single, one-pound egg arrives in April or early May. But a day at most after the egg is laid, the female gives it to the male to keep warm (*opposite*), and in another 12 hours the female is gone, making for the sea to break the fast she has kept for a month. The water by now is perhaps 60 miles away, new sea ice having formed as the winter deepened. The male, which has also fasted since leaving the ocean, must protect the egg until the female's return some 60 days hence. The male then leaves for the sea, having gone without food for about three months. Emperor males spend much of the brooding time in close-packed huddles, for now the winter storms are raging.

The female returns just as the egg is ready to hatch. Fat once more from fishing, she also has a store of extra food which she regurgitates into the mouth of the chick. But for all this parental care, only a fourth of the chicks that hatch may live through the next frozen months; the parents must make the trip to the sea again and again to get food. Finally the summer comes and the now-fledged young accompany their parents to frolic and feed in the sunny, fish-bearing sea.

A BESIEGED MALE is fought over by two embattled female emperors. In the top picture at left the male ducks out of the way while the females glare at each other over his head. In the center picture the females resort to violence, vigorously slapping at each other with their flippers while the male stands aside with resigned detachment. In the bottom picture the victorious female (*left*) stands chest to chest with the hard-won prize and warbles the penguin love song.

A DUTIFUL MALE begins to settle his warm abdomen down on an egg cradled on his thickly webbed feet while the female watches the way the single product of their mating is handled. The male holds the egg for about 63 days while the female goes off to sea and fishes. During his enforced fast the male will lose 25 to 40 per cent of his body weight.

A BABY-SITTING EMPEROR looks over a flock of young much as a top sergeant might survey a squad of recruits. The chicks gather in nurseries under loose adult supervision between the ages of four and nine weeks. They retain their soft, gray down and owl-like eye markings until four to five months old. All this time both parents may be away fishing.

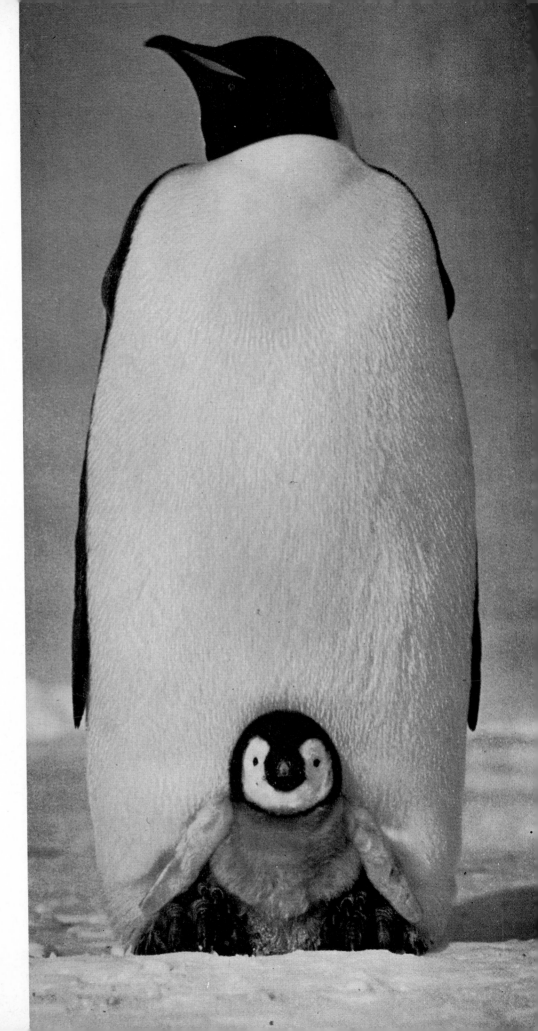

A BABY EMPEROR peers out from its nestling place under its parent's warm fold of abdominal skin (*right*). It will spend its first several weeks riding about on its father's or mother's large flat feet.

MILITARY PRECISION rules a rookery of king penguins as they incubate their eggs on South Georgia Island. While brooding, the kings stand almost exactly a flipper's length apart and, except for a few eccentrics, face the same way in the same stiff, upright position. Like emperor penguins, kings produce one egg, which they balance on their feet and

warm with their stomachs, the males and females taking turns during the eight-week incubation period. King penguins closely resemble emperors and appear almost as large but they are only half as heavy. Living in the less severe climate of the islands north of Antarctica, they do not need the solid, heat-conserving bulk of the emperor to survive.

ON KERGUELEN ISLAND, 2,600 MILES BELOW AUSTRALIA, A BULL ELEPHANT SEAL INFLATES ITS 15-INCH SNOUT IN A LUSTY ROAR.

The Ugly Elephant Seal

Of all the pinnipedian (fin-footed) group of aquatic mammals—seals, sea lions, walruses—the biggest and probably the ugliest is the sea elephant, or elephant seal. The record subantarctic specimen was a male 21 feet 4 inches long which weighed four tons. Another species inhabits the coastal islands of southern and Lower California. The machine age brought the animal near extinction, for its blubber made even better lubricating oil than that of the sperm whale. Large bull seals yielded more than 200 gallons of oil. Petroleum and protective legislation spurred a comeback of the species. With this resurgence, the bull elephant seals continue to collaborate zealously. A prime male may acquire a harem of up to 150 females and is always ready to battle for yet another (*opposite*).

THE TRUNK USUALLY HANGS LIMP

A BATTLE OF BULLS begins (*top, right*) as one approaches a female while another swims in to make his bid. Then (*center*) six tons or more of seal flesh clash and slash with their sharp teeth. At bottom, the loser retires from the contest while the victor lets out a roar before he claims his prize.

A NEWBORN SEAL, still birth-wet (*left*), looks for its first meal. At birth the elephant seal pup has brownish-black fur, which turns grayish or dark yellowish-brown when the seal grows older.

A WRIGGLING BABY eases the itch of its first molt (*opposite*) by rubbing on the beach. In its annual molt the elephant seal sheds its fur and outer skin, becoming a groaning, gurgling pink monster.

A MASTERFUL BULL embraces one member of its harem with a flipper while following its usual custom of snoozing away the daytime hours, waiting for night to eat. Voracious but with sharp, widely spaced teeth unfit for chewing, the seals must swallow their small-fish diet alive. In search of fish, they can dive deep for three to seven minutes.

A YOUNG BULL WALRUS rests its bulk on a rocky islet in the Bering Sea. Walruses are born with nails on their flippers and with mustaches, but their tusks do not grow long enough for clam digging until they are two years old. Until then, cubs depend for food on their mothers' milk and cling tightly to their mothers' necks when in the water.

A COLONY OF WALRUSES SPRAWLS ON A ROCKY ALASKAN BEACH. USUALLY AMIABLE, WALRUSES ROAR AND BELLOW IF DISTURBED

The Wondrous Walrus

The walrus is one of Nature's comedians. Vast and shapeless—a bull may weigh as much as 3,000 pounds—it is a relative of the seal with the wrinkled skin of an old oak, absurdly short flippers, tusks that look like outsize buck teeth, a soup-strainer mustache and the bleary eyes of an aging roué. But the walrus is far sprier than it looks. It can swim tirelessly, gliding along with the easy majesty of a blimp, and maneuver safely in heavy surf near jagged rocks. Using its tusks as a clam rake and its mustache as a mud strainer,

the walrus can scoop hundreds of small shellfish, its favorite food, off the ocean floor for one meal. Highly gregarious, walruses almost always live in groups. Their strong community spirit has made it easy for man to prey on them because they will go to the aid of a wounded fellow instead of swimming to safety. Thus hunters can butcher whole colonies for their hides, tusks and blubber. Once common in the far north, the walrus has now retreated to small areas of northern Greenland, the Bering Sea and the Arctic Ocean.

97

GREAT BULL WALRUSES wallow in the rough waters off the
rocky coast of Alaska. They may live on both sides of the
Bering Strait and often swim its 55 miles of open water.

King of the Ice

The polar bear is the undisputed ruler of a vast and desolate arctic domain. Born likely as not in a snow cave out on the ice pack, a polar bear may never see land but spend its entire life traveling across the pack ice in search of food. Most carnivorous of all bears, its favorite prey is the seal, which it stalks with persistence and guile. Where no ice hummocks provide cover, the bear will crawl forward silently on its belly until near enough to pounce. It can crush a seal's skull with one blow of its great paw. When seal-hunting is poor, it will attack foxes, baby walruses, sea birds —anything alive that invades its kingdom, even man.

Polar bears were the terror of Eskimo hunters before the Eskimos had rifles, for a hungry bear, able to lope for short periods at 25 miles an hour, can overtake a running man. Sometimes growing to an immense 1,600 pounds, the polar bear has dense and oily fur that allows it to hunt even in the depths of winter—only the pregnant females dig dens and become dormant —and to swim without ill effect in the freezing arctic waters.

IN FREEZING WATER, a polar bear crosses an open lead in the ice. Longer and slimmer than other bears, they are strong, tireless swimmers and do not hesitate to set off across 20 miles of rough open water to find better hunting.

ON NEW-FORMED ICE, two polar bears gingerly cross from one old ice floe to another. Rough, leathery pads on the bottoms of their large paws help them grip ice while thick fur between their toes provides extra support on deep snow.

The Unicorn of the Arctic

Of all the odd, improbable animals that inhabit the polar regions, the narwhal seems most clearly to be a creature from legend. A warm-blooded mammal that swims like a fish, has a blowhole and emits shrill whistles and hoarse bellows, it also grows an eight-to-nine-foot tusk straight out of its upper jaw. During the Middle Ages, credulous people seeing a narwhal tusk took it to be the single horn of that famous mythical beast, the unicorn. Many narwhal tusks, washed ashore or brought home by mariners, found their way into medieval apothecary shops, for powdered unicorn horn was reputed to be an excellent specific against all diseases and a sure antidote for poisons. But although the medicinal value of its tusk is nil, the narwhal is real and swims in considerable numbers in the cold arctic waters. A fully grown male may reach a length of 20 feet,

A 20-FOOT NARWHAL WITH A TAPERING, POINTED TUSK GLIDES SWIFTLY AMONG BROKEN PIECES OF ARCTIC PACK ICE. LIKE ALL

including tusk, and occasionally grows twin tusks rather than one. Rarely, the female has a tusk too. When a narwhal does have a pair of tusks, their spirals always twist in the same direction; on goats and all other animals with paired spiral structures, the spirals go in opposite directions.

Sociable and playful, narwhals go in groups, appear to talk to each other and often engage in harmless fencing matches with their tusks.

Except for this play, narwhals do not seem to use the tusks at all, neither attacking other animals with them nor ramming boats, as swordfish sometimes do. They catch their food, mainly cuttlefish, under water. Once hunted by whalers, the narwhal is still choice game for Eskimos, who render its blubber for oil, eat its flesh, use its tough hide for thongs and carve the ivory of the hollow tusks into tools and small objects of art.

SEAGOING MAMMALS, IT MUST COME TO THE SURFACE FOR AIR, AND OFTEN RESTS BY LAYING ITS TUSK ON THE EDGE OF A FLOE

5

The World
of the Tundra

NORTH from the limit of trees to the shores of the Arctic Ocean, the wide plains and moors of the tundra stretch around the North Pole. The word "tundra" is an ancient Finno-Ugrian one taken by the Russians from the Lapps, and is understood by all northern peoples to refer to the area of five million square miles, a tenth of the earth's land surface, which separates the sea and ice from the forests. This is the typical arctic land, an exotic life zone at once barren and abundant.

Though littered with lakes and swampy ground, the tundra has a desert climate. Its average yearly precipitation is only about eight inches, yet from the air it often appears as more water than land, and travel across it in the summer is wet and arduous. Unlike other deserts, the tundra maintains its water because its cold air cannot easily absorb water vapor, and because of the permafrost a few inches below the surface, which thwarts normal drainage. Its most important source of water is this permafrost, which is gradually releasing its ancient reserves of ice in the annual surface thaws. All this moisture is more than enough for the thin mantle of vegetation that spreads over the land.

In the summer, tundra ponds and streams are the nesting grounds for myriad waterfowl; its grasslands are dotted with the nests of land birds and undermined by the burrows of lemmings. Overland pass wandering bands of large grazing animals. Its lakes and rivers abound with muskrats, nibbling on succulent water plants, and with fish supported by the insects and their larvae: grayling, great northern pike, lake trout, whitefish, smelt, ling, inconnu, lake herring and arctic char. The tundra is a rich hunting ground for the carnivores—owls swooping on lemmings, foxes feeding on bird eggs, wolves chasing caribou, and barren-ground grizzlies which apparently regard every living thing as their meat. The short growing season forces the plants to race for maturity before the frost and in quick succession flowers unfold their bright blossoms, ripen their seeds, flush with autumn coloration, wither and return to dormancy.

In winter this abundant life disappears and the land is frozen and forlorn. Whatever snow falls, remains until the following summer except where the ground is swept bare by the wind. Thick ice forms on the lakes and rivers, making travel easy. The waterfowl have flown south, the lemmings have gone under the snow, the caribou have returned to the shelter of the forests. In a few localities the dark musk oxen remain, easily mistaken for boulders from a distance. The daylight lasts for only a few hours; but the moon reflecting from the white snow provides ample light. At long intervals a loud "boom" is heard as ice cracks on a pond or stream.

THE tundra is the creation of intense cold and glaciers. Tundra regions bordered the great continental ice sheets of the Pleistocene era as they spread south over the present Temperate Zones. Our cave-dwelling ancestors of central Europe were familiar with conditions on the tundra, and lived by hunting its herd animals. As the glaciers retreated to the north, the tundra followed them. Today it has invaded the region leveled and scoured by the vanished ice sheets, and supports an array of life forms which are slowly covering up the damage.

Yet the remains of the glacial wreckage are everywhere apparent. Forbidding mounds of lichen-covered rubble attest the terminal moraines of individual offshoots of the ice. Eskers, looking like railroad embankments, wander for miles, tracing the paths of the debris-laden streams within the vanished glaciers. The ground is strewn with erratic boulders, carried from distant regions and dropped by the ice. The contour of the land itself, flattened and filled with depressions, is a record of the recent cataclysm.

The results of the intense cold are equally spectacular. Frost, interrupted at the surface only during the short summer months, invades the bedrock wherever it is exposed. Water which has seeped into the rock during thaws freezes and expands, often shattering the stone into thousands of sharp boulders. These can cover immense areas, and although the debris may be covered with lichens it offers no hospitality to higher vegetation and is a chaotic obstacle to travel.

One of the strange features of frost action is its tendency to sort the debris of annual freezing and thawing into coarse and fine particles, separated by regular intervals. When this occurs on a slope, the coarse and fine particles form stripes running downhill. The peculiar "striped ground," often tinted by vegetation, may be seen from a great distance.

When the surface is level, the sorting action of frost moves coarser particles

A TUNDRA TITAN, the barren-ground grizzly roams over north Canada. Like its southern cousin, the grizzly of the western U.S. and Canada, it is omnivorous, eating both plants and animals. The bear above is pawing for grubs under a stone.

out to the borders of polygon-shaped patches of fine material. These polygons vary in diameter from a few inches to over 100 yards, and may occur in clusters miles across. The coarser and finer materials offer different habitats for plants, so the outlines of the polygons look like a patterned garden. Occasionally polygons are bordered by large stones and rocks, left standing on edge by the frost.

In some dry lakes and stream beds, weird, conical-shaped mounds of earth, known as pingos, jut as high as 300 feet from the level ground. They are also called frost heaves. Though their origins are still uncertain, most have a core of blue-white ice, and a spring may flow from fissures at the top.

Another deforming action of frost on the land is a phenomenon called solifluction. During the warm months, the ice in the top layer of the tundra soil melts, and the sodden layer of earth sits precariously upon a deeper layer of solidly frozen ground. When this happens on a slope—and almost all land has at least a slight incline—the top layer of soil tends to flow downhill. The rate of slippage is usually slow and uneven, perhaps only a few inches a year, but any movement may be disastrous for immobile plants. Often whole colonies of plants downhill from a patch of unstable soil will be slowly buried alive. Some of the plants in the moving layer are equally unlucky; their roots are sheared and their stems snapped as one part of the ground moves slightly faster than the other. Or a plant which was thriving in some well-watered spot up the hill will find itself transplanted over a buried boulder, unable to put its roots down to subsurface water.

The plants themselves often add to their own misfortunes. The first plant species to move into a "frost scar," an area of bare earth or gravel, are sturdy colonizing plants such as the purple saxifrage and the woodrush. In a few years these pioneers create little pockets of shelter where other plants can grow. Then the newcomers crowd out the colonizing species and form a dense mat over the once-bare ground. But such a layer of vegetation breeds its own destruction because its shade reduces the amount of warmth reaching the soil underneath. Each summer the depth of the melted layer of topsoil in which the plants grow gets shallower. As the permafrost rises toward the surface, it pushes up the soil, disturbing the roots and exposing the earth to wind and water erosion. Soon plants and soil are gone and the land is bare again, ready for a new set of pioneers. Such a cycle does not occur overnight, but in ecological terms it is surprisingly swift, going from bare ground to bare ground again in a span of only 50 years.

DESPITE these perils, the treacherous soils of the tundra are home to about 900 species of plants. This is the land of the little plant, with only a few species growing more than ankle-high. Of course, there are no upright trees; the few species north of timber line—mostly willows, elders and birches—are stunted. Only near tree line in sheltered valleys along flowing streams do many of the trees get head-high. But these dwarf plants often live to old age. An arctic willow may have 400 annual rings crowded into its one-inch "trunk."

Apart from the short stature which they have in common, tundra plants have radically different tolerances for moisture, mineral nutrients, winter wind and cold, soil acidity and erosional forces. In the marshes, for instance, the main vegetation is likely to be a bed of soggy sphagnum moss, punctuated here and there by hummocks of a tough grass that spreads

A GHOSTLY HUNTER, the snowy owl has white plumage which blends into the tundra landscape. Lemmings are its chief prey. When the lemmings are scarce, the owls migrate to seek other food. They have been seen as far south as Maryland.

through the acid muck with underground runners. The standing marsh water forms the breeding ground for the insects that harass the tundra animals. In other wet meadows there are stands of a grasslike plant called arctic cotton, which bears its seeds in white, fluffy bolls. At the dry end of the moisture scale are vast well-drained areas covered with masses of coarse gravel and boulders. Nothing but lichens survive on the bare rock surfaces, but in the crevices small pockets of wind-blown soil and lichen remains collect and hold a little water. Mosses invade these stony pockets and in time form a base on which small flowering plants can grow.

Between the extremes of marsh and gravel field are vast intermediate areas, neither drenched nor dry. Close to timber line these are often carpeted by an extraordinary yellowish lichen which is misnamed "reindeer-moss." This is the prairie grass of the Arctic, furnishing winter graze for the caribou. Also blanketing many tundra hollows are the arctic varieties of some plants familiar in southern latitudes: cranberry, blueberry and heather. In general they can take hold only where snow accumulates in winter, giving some protection from the withering cold.

BLACK SPRUCE is by nature a stately, upright tree. The specimen above has been forced to creep along the ground by cold wind and drought which beset it on an exposed hillside just above tree line in Canada's Northwest Territories.

MANY of the tundra plants can be seen far from the Arctic, on the alpine heights of the southern Rocky Mountains, the Cascade-Sierra Nevada Range and the northern Appalachians. A few plants have close relatives on high mountains the world over. This is because the world's high altitudes and its high latitudes share such important environmental factors—all adverse—as extreme cold, wind and drought.

A census of the plant species in all of the north-polar regions would turn up about 400 which are common to the tundras of Canada, Siberia and north Europe. These are the so-called circumpolar plants. True, plant seeds can be wind-blown or carried long distances by birds. But when so many species occur on both sides of a body of water, it is a strong sign that they crossed over on a land bridge. Scientists now know that such a causeway perhaps 1,300 miles wide joined Alaska and Siberia during the last ice age only about 10,000 years ago. Even today, north of Siberia, shallow water extends for miles beyond sight of land and it is sometimes impossible to move a rowboat over the bottom. Animal bones taken from these shallows show that they used to be grazing lands.

Many relics of preglacial mammals have been found on the tundra, preserved by the permafrost and the lack of decaying organisms. In Kotzebue Sound on the Bering Sea, and in the dredgings of placer mines, the remains occur in great numbers. Imbedded in cliffs are the bodies, sometimes preserved with skin and fur, of woolly mammoths, rhinoceroses, saber-toothed tigers, super bison, horses and camels. A few of these had been so well refrigerated that their stomachs could be examined. The analysis has shown that tundra vegetation then, 25,000 years ago, was essentially the same as now.

ARCTIC WILLOW is by nature a sprawling plant. Through slow evolution, its species has adapted to life in the north by developing ground-hugging tendencies which allow it, so to speak, to duck the worst of the tundra's cold, drying winds.

The abundance of insect and plant food on the tundra in summer has made it the nesting ground for many species of birds. The almost continuous light enables the parents to gather food night and day—and their fledglings quickly grow to a point where they can fly. In the grasses of river deltas, tundra lakes and ponds, the pintails, teal, baldpates, scaups, goldeneyes, scoters, mergansers and old squaw ducks make their nests. Nothing is more startling in the arctic stillness than the sound of a passing goldeneye whose flight gives the impression of a plane overhead because of the peculiar noise of the wind passing over its wings. Rarely, a pond is found harboring a colony of lovely harlequin ducks. Near the sea, eider ducks build their stone-and-twig nests and line them with down plucked from their breasts. They may be induced to build in little shelters of rocks placed by egg or eider-down collectors.

The Canada goose is common near the big rivers, and snow geese nest in huge colonies. At the mouths of many of the turgid streams of northern Canada thousands of snow geese gather on the mud flats in May, laying their eggs before the ice and snow have disappeared. Sand-hill cranes and other wading birds dance on the river flats, and plover of several varieties nest on the uplands.

Gyrfalcons, ravens and owls are everywhere on the tundra. They are not migratory in the true sense, being equally inclined to move east and west or north and south in their search for food. A severe food shortage will force them down into the temperate regions in winter; snowy owls are often seen in the northern United States.

Of all the birds, the ptarmigan is most truly a tundra creature. This pigeon-sized grouse lives in the north all year round, through good years and bad. In summer it walks over the hillsides picking berries and nipping off the tender new shoots of plants; in winter large flocks gather in protected valleys, particularly where there is a healthy growth of willow. The buds are its chief winter food, and the flesh of the bird takes on the flavor of the willow leaf. Ptarmigan makes good eating for any tundra enemy quick enough to catch it. The bird's chief protection is camouflage, a speckled brown summer plumage and solid white for winter. Ptarmigan fly well, but when they do their camouflage is useless and they are easily spotted by predaceous birds, such as the jaeger, gyrfalcon and snowy owl. So the ptarmigan stay close to the ground; they may not even stir unless nearly trod upon; then they take off with a loud flapping. In winter a frightened ptarmigan is apt to dive straight into a snowbank. These birds are monogamous; they nest on the ground, with the female incubating the eggs while the male wanders off. After the chicks have hatched he returns and stays nearby, ready to decoy danger away from his family.

THE populations of tundra animals repeatedly explode and crash. This is especially true of those that subsist largely on one kind of food, and of small animals that spend all their lives in limited areas. The most notable of these is the little lemming. Its population rises and falls in a predictable cycle—and unpredictably, as everyone knows, lemmings undertake mass wanderings across the tundra. But it has never been demonstrated that they have the legendary instinctive longing to fling themselves into the ocean. Indeed, most lemmings never migrate at all.

The rodent is small and furry, like a stubby mouse. It grows to about five inches long and has brown fur, often striped with yellowish markings. The collared lemming, which wears a golden band around the throat, is the only rodent that changes to an all-white winter coat. In summer lemmings feed upon grasses and busily store the leaves and roots in holes and rock crevices for winter use. In winter they travel about in tunnels under the snow, in a complicated maze which often is the last thing to melt in the spring, leaving a lacy network of ice on the ground.

The forelegs of the lemming are equipped with powerful digging claws, and in summer it digs burrows in the top layer of soil which the sun has thawed. In winter the forefeet are strangely altered, perhaps for tunneling through snow. On the bottom of each of the two middle toes a horny pad forms, which lasts until the following spring, when it gradually loosens and is sloughed off.

Female lemmings deliver their first young when less than six months old, and can produce eight litters a year. Thus the lemming population of any area is capable of swift increase. And the individual lemming is capable of a quixotic courage. Indeed, there is a Scandinavian expression for it— "brave as a lemming." If approached, the rodent will stubbornly hold its ground, chirping and bristling. Obviously this is not practical behavior for such a diminutive animal, and the lemming becomes easy prey for almost any predator that wants to devour him.

In many areas lemmings form the chief item of diet for arctic foxes and for snowy owls, but they are also eaten by wolves, bears, and by the jaeger and the skua, two gull-like birds which have the hunting instincts of hawks. Even the relatively meek caribou may develop an appetite for lemmings in the spring; it chases the hapless rodents and kills them with its hoofs.

In peak population years, the ground in any area seems to be crawling with lemmings—and is soon stripped of plant cover as they move over it. The lemming appears to be a one-track animal once it starts traveling. It keeps going in one compass direction; lakes, streams, mountains, short snow fields and marshes do not hinder its progress. The migrations increase in size as they go. When the lemmings arrive at cultivated land they are a scourge to the farmers; in former days many Scandinavian peasants were convinced that the lemmings which suddenly deluged their land had rained from the sky. In lakes and rivers the lemmings are eaten even by pike and char, among other fish. Those that reach the far side shake themselves like puppies to dry their fur.

A lemming migration is a wonderful thing to watch, and is somewhat like a gigantic school of fish moving in the ocean. While above the fish thousands of screaming sea birds dive and feed, the lemmings are followed by voracious foxes, lynxes and weasels; and in the air flocks of ravens, owls and hawks are gathered for the feast.

No arctic animal, unless it is the wolf through its dog descendants, has been more intimately associated with man than the reindeer of the tundra. In prehistoric times, in the vanguard of the great ice sheets, its range extended far south into France and Spain, to Turkey and China, and to Central America. During the latter stages of the Pleistocene era it often served as the staple food for man, and our forebears were nourished for many thousands of years upon reindeer meat. The reindeer of the Old World and the caribou of the New World are essentially one and the same animal. In North America it is the practice to refer to the wild form as caribou, to the tame form as reindeer. The caribou that range the north appear in three chief varieties: the mountain caribou, the woodland caribou and the barren-ground caribou, the only true tundra type.

The explorers of the 18th and 19th Centuries often reported herds of millions of barren-ground caribou. There are many accounts of herds a mile wide which took several days or even a week to pass. These immense herds no longer exist, and in northern Eurasia they have been replaced almost entirely by tame reindeer. In Alaska there are perhaps 300,000 wild caribou grazing on the arctic slopes, and on the tundra of Canada another 300,000. Until recent years these herds were shrinking. Through wise range management they have been increased to a healthy population in Alaska, and the decline has been checked in northern Canada.

The barren-ground caribou is not a large animal. Mature bulls seldom weigh more than 350 pounds while cows rarely reach 200. Their antlers, however, are large, with spreads up to six feet. During the summer the caribou are gray-brown with occasional splotches of white. When winter comes many of the dark tips of hair break off, leaving a whitish coat. In spring the hair is shed and comes off in great patches, which makes the animal for several weeks a sorry specimen indeed. During this season, a pest called the warble fly lays its eggs on the abdomen of the caribou. The hatched larvae eat their way through the skin and tunnel their way to the back, where they form cysts. Reindeer become frantic when the flies are around and reportedly have stampeded over cliffs in efforts to evade them.

THE caribou is not a graceful animal except when it is running with its head held high and thrust forward. Its feet are enormous, but the big hoofs give it good support in boggy areas and on crusted snow. The nose is covered with hair, probably to protect the muzzle when probing for lichens under the snow.

If the adults are ungraceful, the calves are ungainly. Their legs are disproportionately long, the front ones straight, the back ones bent out at the hock as if to provide tripod support for an unbalanced body. The hoofs are broad, like those of the parents, and in both adult and young the ankle tendons "click" as they trot. Caribou shed their antlers annually, the bulls in early winter, the cows in early spring, and new ones begin to grow at once. As the bulls grow up, their antlers become heavier and more highly branched until the animal is about eight years old, after which they decline.

Caribou follow a regular seasonal rhythm in their movements across the tundra. At midyear, they wander in scattered bands, grazing sporadically, desperate from the attacks of flies and mosquitoes. They may get relief by going to the windy seacoasts, the islands of the north, or high exposed ground. Toward autumn they begin to cluster in larger herds, and to move south in growing numbers until the marginal forest is reached. They enter this thin forest for about a month, then come out onto the tundra again for the rutting season. By now the bulls have built up a thick layer of back fat, but most of this disappears during the rutting combats. At the end of October they return to the forest to stay for the winter.

In April the cows start their trek north to the calving grounds, which may be a great distance away. The males remain behind in the forest to join them a month later, after the calves have been born. As soon as the young are strong enough to travel—a matter of a few days—the herd moves farther north to the cool, windy summer pastures of grasses and sedges. Wherever they go, in every season, they are trailed by marauding wolves.

The rarest of large northern mammals is the musk ox, formerly circumpolar in its distribution, but now confined to North America and Greenland, with transplants on Nunivak Island in the Bering Sea, Spitsbergen and the mountains of central Norway. The musk ox was driven far to the

IN RELENTLESS MIGRATION, a band of lemmings plunges into the water. This six-inch arctic rodent has periodic population explosions and must migrate to new areas in search of food. Rather than change direction, the lemmings try to swim across large rivers, lakes or even arms of the sea, where they drown. But this is not the mass suicide of legend.

south by the great ice sheets of the Pleistocene era, and its bones have been found as far south as Kentucky. In the Stone Age caves in France it occurs not only in the bone heaps which archaeologists have picked over, but also in cave paintings and rock carvings. By the time the Stone Age ended, the musk ox was exterminated from Eurasia.

Although there are some Norse references to an animal of northeast Greenland which could only be the musk ox, it was first described in modern literature from the area west of Hudson Bay in the latter part of the 17th Century. It was referred to as a peculiar buffalo, and no reference was made to musk. All of the large ruminants emit a musk odor during the rutting season, and this one is no exception.

The musk ox grows to about the size of a small cow: a full-grown bull stands about four and a half feet tall at the shoulders and weighs about 900 pounds. The females are a third smaller. The weight is concentrated in the forequarters, which are surmounted by a muscular hump. Long, shaggy, brown hair covers the body and blows in the slightest breeze; it gives the animal a heavy, clumsy appearance which belies the agile body underneath. The musk ox has true hollow horns, permanently attached to the skull. On the male the horns grow from the center of the forehead, while on the female they start at the sides of the head. The winter undercoat of quviut is shed late in May and peels off the animal in great sheets which catch on willow bushes and blow about the tundra.

The musk ox is no migrant and the major difference between its winter and summer ranges is that in winter it feeds in the snow-free pastures of the wind-swept upland, while in summer it favors the low-lying willow thickets along the streams. A complacent animal, it conserves a great deal of energy by spending much of each day lying flat upon the ground in slumber.

The herds may consist of a few animals or of bands as large as 50. The nucleus is a harem of cows with their calves, under the protection of the lead bull. As autumn comes, the bull must fight competing males to keep possession of his harem. The actual leader of the herd in its movements about the tundra and the grazing grounds is an old cow, usually with calf. A curious feature of musk-ox social life is the fact that a number of male animals will band together and form exclusive bull herds, each with its own leader. But some bulls are banished from herds altogether. They amble alone over the tundra, apparently content in their private ways of life.

To civilized man, the tundra appears to be a place of loneliness. Its frost-tortured ground stretches endlessly without a tree, often without a sign of any living thing to break its monotony. It was this that led the earliest explorers to call the tundra "the barrens." Of course the loneliness is an illusion: to the few Indians and Eskimos who make the tundra their home it is a source of life—and the source of contentment that every man finds in his native land.

A Caribou Indian once expressed this to a priest who was telling him of the Christian idea of Heaven: "My father, you have told me that Heaven is very beautiful. Is it more beautiful than the country of the musk ox in summer, when sometimes the wind blows over the lakes, and sometimes the water is blue and the loons cry very often? That is beautiful, and if Heaven is still more beautiful, my heart will be glad, and I shall be content to rest there till I am very old."

THIS IS TUNDRA—LOW HILLS PUDDLED BY ICE-WATER LAKES STRETCHING TO THE HORIZON IN CANADA'S NORTHWEST TERRITORIES

The Populous Barrens

Early explorers came on the treeless landscape of the far north and turned back; they called it the barren land, or simply the barrens. But men have revised their ideas of the area, finding the tundra rich in life: plants so dense they form mats under-foot, animal herds so vast they blot out all the earth in sight. Their home is a fifth of all the Northern Hemisphere's land.

THE TUNDRA BEGINS at the edge of a grove of evergreens north of Canada's Great Bear Lake. Above this tree line, the frozen soil and cold summers stunt all tree growth.

Frozen Figures on the Land

Patterns formed by frost, rocks and plants interrupt the rolling regularity of hills and lakes of the tundra country. In the south a few swirls of trees decorate the land. But the immense force of freezing and thawing water is the north's chief sculptor. Only about eight inches of precipitation fall each year over most of the tundra—little more than on the Mojave Desert. Because the soil is frozen, the water does not seep down into the earth. Most of it collects in low places to form thousands of tundra lakes. It also flows into the soil, where it freezes and heaves up rocks, sometimes in the waffle pattern shown at the right.

A POLYGONAL GRID IS LAID OVER THIS LOW-LYING AREA

A PINGO, or giant frost-heave, towers 300 feet over the tundra. Pingos occur where underground water wells up and freezes into plugs of ice when it nears the surface.

STONE RINGS in Greenland are six feet across. They result from freezing and thawing of soil. Freezing nudges the rocks outward; in thaws, they are not pulled back as far.

OF NORTH-CENTRAL CANADA. ROCKS THROWN UP BY FROST ACTION FORM A SYSTEM OF DIKES WHICH TRAP SMALL POOLS OF WATER

GLACIAL GOUGES are filled with drifting snow on the central Canadian tundra. They were chiseled in the bedrock by boulders borne in the advancing ice sheet of the last ice age.

A MEANDERING STREAM traces its crooked course into Hudson Bay, leaving a muddy oxbow lake formed from one of its loops. Only a few sluggish rivers drain the tundra.

A SHRINKING GLACIER ON AXEL HEIBERG ISLAND IN NORTH CANADA SENDS OUT SPRAYS OF WATER, MUDDIED BY THE DIRT IN THE ICE

The Retreating Ice

As the ponderous ice sheet of the last glacial age backed off to the north, it withdrew first from the United States, next from southern Canada and then—about 9,000 years ago—from the north Canadian tundra. The glaciers' retreat is still visible at many places. On the tundra itself winter is still long (mid-September to mid-June) and spring comes reluctantly, but scientists have found a warming trend. The edge of the permafrost—the area where the ground never thaws—is moving north a few hundred feet a year. Much of the tundra may be at the threshold of the evolution into fertile land that long ago blessed other regions, after the ice went north.

THIN SPRING ICE, formed on a lake during the cold night (*opposite*), glows yellow in the morning sun. At the upper left is a tussock of grass growing along the swampy shore.

CANDLED ICE, a palisade of crystals four feet high (*below*), formed over a Baffin Island river and was blown ashore. A candled effect occurs when partly melted ice is refrozen.

REINDEER MOSS is a many-branched lichen growing to a height of six inches or more. Often it twines into dense mats over large areas, making winter pasture for the caribou.

The Colonizing Lichens

The lichen is not one plant but two, a successful partnership which survives in some of the toughest environments on the face of the earth. It thrives in the cold, dry, rocky tundra, where it furnishes food for grazing animals and gradually produces new soil in which other plants can gain a roothold.

One half of the lichen partnership is a fungus, the other half a green alga. The fungus partner anchors itself to a rock and generates a mass of spongy tissue which holds large quantities of water. The alga lives inside this moist shelter, produces food by photosynthesis and shares this nourishment with the fungus.

Lichens grow at an extremely slow rate, but over the centuries their decayed remains turn into the raw materials of fertile earth. Moreover, some lichens produce chemicals which disintegrate the surface of rock into fine soil particles.

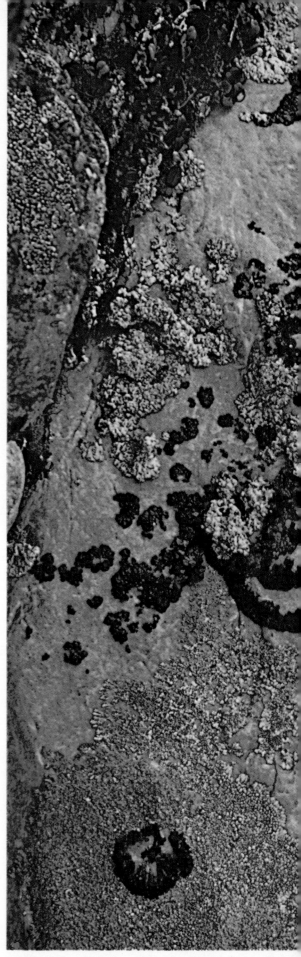

TWO LICHENS, ONE A GREEN CRUST, THE OTHER A BLACK

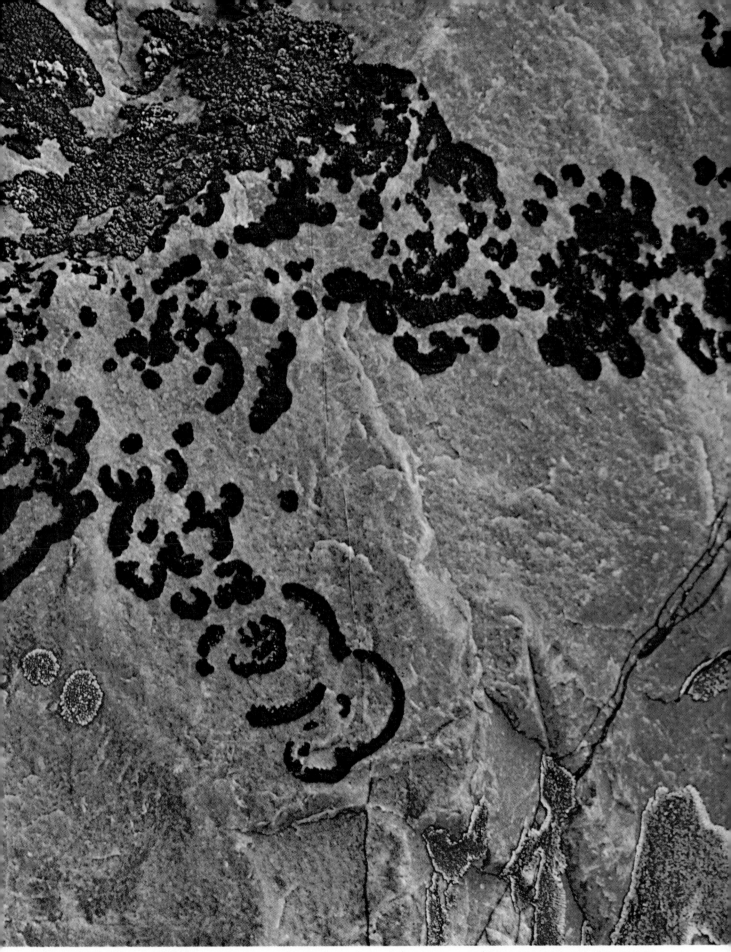

SCROLLWORK, CLING TO A BOULDER. LICHENS GROW SO SLOWLY THAT IN 10 YEARS THESE PLANTS MIGHT NOT SPREAD PERCEPTIBLY

AN ARCTIC POPPY erupts in a fragile tracery of six-inch
flower stalks rising above its cluster of foliage. Shining in
the sunlight are the beards of downy hairs which insulate
the surfaces of the plant from the killing cold. The arctic
poppy is one of the rare plants which can flower and produce ripe seeds for a new generation in less than a month.

Flowers of the Cold Desert

It is neither bitter cold nor desertlike drought but the brief and wildly uncertain growing season that poses the chief peril to larger tundra plants in their struggle to survive. There are only about eight weeks in July and August when the temperature stays above freezing. Even in these months, when the thermometer may climb to the 90s, there may be days and nights when it drops under 32. So tundra plants, like those on high mountains, trail close to the ground and have heavy stems and leaves to take advantage of the life-giving heat of the sun. Nearly all these plants are perennials, which insures a species' survival when the short summer is interrupted by a killing frost. The perennials bear their flowers over many years, lest one cold summer wipe them out. Many plants do not even flower; they reproduce by sending out runners or underground shoots.

A SEA BLUEBELL, relative of the forget-me-not, blooms on the Arctic Ocean's sandy shore. Like many tundra plants, it grows in a compact cushion to conserve precious warmth.

A SPIDER SAXIFRAGE, GROWING IN MOIST MOSS, THRUSTS OUT A HALF-DOZEN RUNNERS WHICH WILL MATURE INTO NEW PLANTS

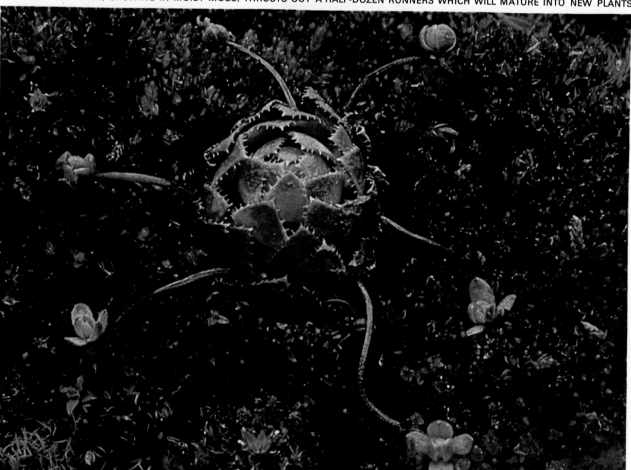

Life-Preserving Colors

Vague shadows flit over the snow-covered winter tundra; a bright eye glows from a brown lump pressed against the summer landscape. Such are the few visible signs of the profusion of small animals that unobtrusively populates the tundra. On this shelterless land, more than anywhere else on earth, animals insure their survival by changing color to blend into the seasonal background.

ARCTIC HARES, SELDOM SEEN IN LARGE GROUPS, GATHER ON A

SLOPE ON ELLESMERE ISLAND TO BASK IN THE SPRING SUN. FAR-NORTHERN HARES KEEP THEIR WHITE COATS THE YEAR ROUND

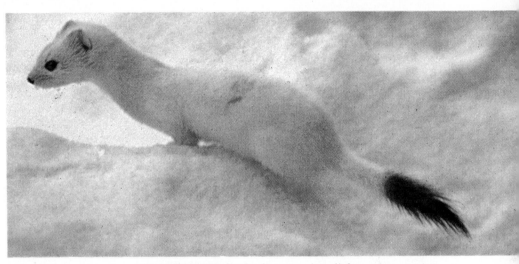

ON THE PROWL for food, an ermine slinks across a snow-bank. It spends most of its time under the snow in winter; in summer it wears a brown coat and is known as a weasel.

CHANGEABLE PTARMIGAN never leave the tundra. The bird at left has started to change its white winter coat to summer brown; the bird above has completed the change.

123

A FROZEN CARCASS of a musk ox makes a meal for an arctic wolf. Though seldom the equal of a healthy 800-pound bull, a wolf will occasionally bring down a feeble animal cast out from the herd. Like many tundra species, the arctic wolf, a powerful predator weighing as much as 175 pounds, is lighter in color than its southern relatives.

A HERD OF MUSK OXEN ON CORNWALLIS ISLAND FORMS AN IMPENETRABLE SHOULDER-TO-SHOULDER WALL AS A PHOTOGRAPHER

The Declining Musk Ox

Until men with guns came, the musk ox was the lord of the tundra. Its heavy coat protects it from winter cold and from summer hordes of bloodsucking insects. Its heavy hoofs can easily break the ice crusts covering its favorite willow twigs. When danger threatens, the bulls form a line in front of the cows and young. Their massive horns are a match for wolves and even Eskimos with primitive weapons. But when the defense line forms and the heads go down, the musk oxen are an easy target for any rifleman. Hunting has decimated them; only 7,000 survive.

MUSK-OX REMAINS fertilize the thin arctic soil. Around the skeleton lichens, mosses and young seed plants have sprung up, nourished by minerals leached from the bones.

APPROACHES. WHEN A PACK OF WOLVES ATTACKS A HERD, THE BULLS FORM A HOLLOW SQUARE, THEIR COWS AND CALVES INSIDE

A CALF RESTS DURING A PAUSE IN A CARIBOU HERD MIGRATION

The Wandering Caribou

A half million wild caribou still roam over the North American tundra. Another half million domesticated caribou, or reindeer, are cared for by Lapp and Eskimo herders.

Actually caribou do not spend the entire year on the tundra. They winter south of the tree line and hurry northward with the coming of spring, seeking forage and trying to avoid the clouds of mosquitoes and flies which torment them. The calves are born in the north and make the trek south to the sheltering forests as fall approaches.

CARIBOU BULLS like these have huge antlers, shed each winter, regrown each spring. The bull at left is shedding the "velvet" which covers the new antlers till they harden.

A CARIBOU HERD of about 5,000 animals (*right*), one of the largest seen in years, flows over the Canadian tundra. Caribou use the same migration routes year after year.

126

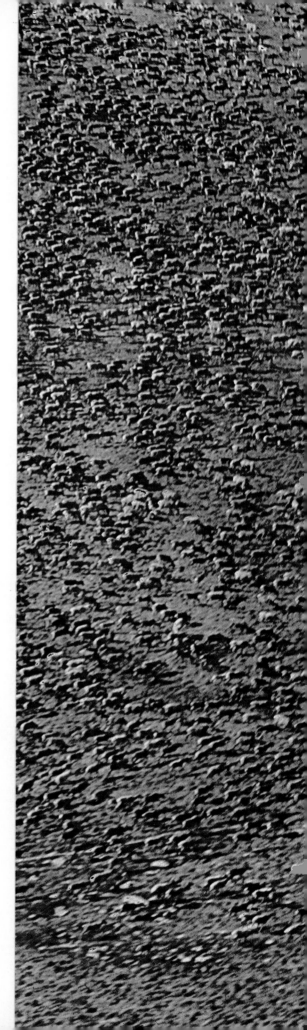

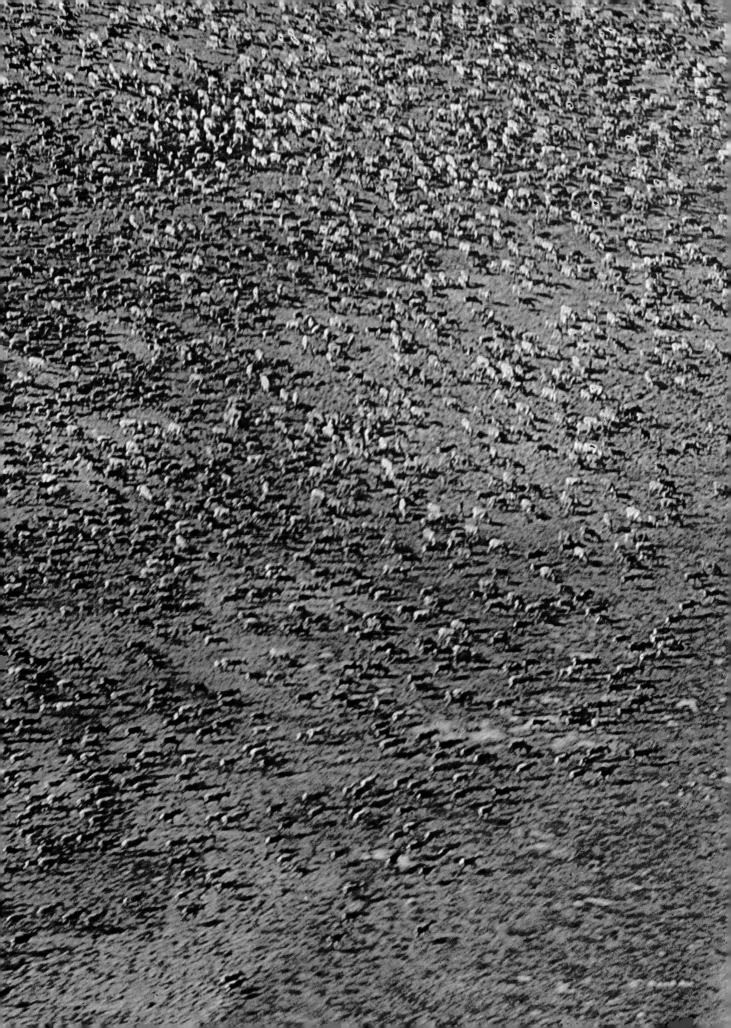

6

Man at High Latitudes

SAVE for the frigid fortress of the Antarctic, no great region on earth seems
less inviting to most men than the Arctic. Only in recent years has science
made it possible for civilized men to live there with some measure of their
accustomed comfort and security. Yet primitive peoples have been living
in the Arctic for thousands of years. They are more than the hardiest people
on earth. Among them also are—or were, until civilized men began changing their patterns of life—some of the happiest of humans. Their survival is
a supreme example of human adaptability. Their happiness, springing from
a philosophy and way of life that civilized people have long since abandoned,
is a triumph of the human spirit.

As preservers of Stone Age life in an awesome environment, the natives of
the Arctic have long fascinated anthropologist-explorers. But a knowledge of
their methods of life has now become of wide practical importance. In defense of freedom or in search of new wealth or a new start, more and more
people from the south are going and will be going to the Arctic. In no other
primitive area have newcomers had to adopt so many native techniques.

Yet it still may be wondered why the arctic aborigines went there in the first place. The natural supposition would be that they must have been driven by lack of living space, by some great natural disaster like the drying up of the Sahara region, or by human enemies. But the available evidence indicates that they went voluntarily.

Native life in the north not only preserves much of the Stone Age, but also suggests what ice-age life must have been like. And it is precisely the last ice age that seems to be the key to arctic settlement. When a good part of the Northern Hemisphere was covered by ice thousands of feet thick, men of the Old Stone Age grew accustomed to hunting in an arctic environment. The advancing glaciers had driven southward such arctic animals as the reindeer and the musk ox. When the glaciers retreated, the animals followed them, and some men apparently followed the animals. Stone Age man lived by hunting and food-gathering; the Arctic abounds in game animals of land, sea and sky, and in summer has some edible plants.

CIVILIZATION means cities and farming, both lacking among hunting people compelled to roam widely in search of food. But civilization is not to be confused with culture—the complex of beliefs, customs, institutions, tools and techniques by which a society lives—and the arctic peoples developed some of the world's most ingenious and interesting cultures.

One of the most striking features of these cultures is their uniformity. Although the arctic peoples are spread over a vast area and are relatively few in number, their clothing, some of their hunting and cooking instruments and techniques, their social organization and other cultural elements bear a marked similarity to each other, whether in Siberia, Europe or North America. Thus, both the Eskimos of Banks Island, in the western part of the Canadian Arctic Archipelago, and the Lapps of northern Scandinavia prefer the skin of a caribou-reindeer fawn killed in August, with the hair turned in, for inner clothing. Both prefer the skin of a yearling killed in August, with the hair turned out, for coats or the hooded jackets called parkas.

In winter, most Eskimos live in earthen huts that are partly dug underground. These dwellings much resemble the huts once used by the Lapps and the Samoyeds, Koryaks and Chukchi of northern Siberia. The same types of snowshoes are used by the Eskimos and Indians and by Asiatic tribes. Such similarities, as well as racial resemblances, indicate that many of these people originated in a single area. Anthropologists generally believe that this area was central Asia.

Probably the oldest group of arctic people are the Paleo-Asiatics of northeastern Siberia. These include the Yukaghirs, Chukchi and Koryaks, all of whom are believed to be the remnants of an ancient group of Mongolian-type people. Mainly nomads, these tribes were originally hunters and fishermen who have largely turned to reindeer herding.

Most aborigines of the Siberian Arctic belong to the Ural-Altaic group, which includes the Tungus, Yakuts and the Samoyeds. The Tungus, related to steppe-dwelling people in the south, were among the first of this group to migrate northward. Their territory was later invaded by the Yakuts, who are the largest aboriginal group in Siberia, and then by the Cossacks in the early 1600s.

Like other arctic aborigines, the Yakuts show an unequaled ability to endure cold, hunger, fatigue and lack of sleep—the latter especially in summer "when the sun does not sleep." Stripping naked at 60° below zero,

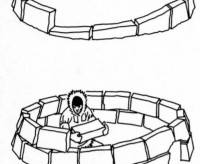

BUILDING OF AN IGLOO is outlined in the three drawings above. Firmly packed snow with an even consistency is best. Blocks 36 by 18 by 6 inches are cut with a broad-bladed knife 14 to 20 inches long.

• First a round foundation is laid; 10 feet is a good diameter. Three of the foundation blocks are cut into a ramp to begin the spiral wall. As the structure is built up from the inside, each layer is leaned slightly more inward. If each new block is firmly fitted, the dome will not collapse.

• When the igloo is two or three blocks high, a temporary door is cut into one side, for construction purposes only.

• Finally the king block, carefully cut to fit the hole, is lowered into the last gap in the dome. The cracks are then filled with snow. The side doorway is closed and a permanent entry begun (opposite page).

they lie down to sleep in the open with only their own clothes for a covering and a small wood fire to keep them from freezing. Snow falls and melts on exposed portions of their bodies without seeming to disturb them. Charles Darwin reported similar adaptation to cold among the Fuegians, a now virtually extinct subantarctic people inhabiting the southern tip of South America. He wrote: " . . . a woman, who was suckling a recently born child, came one day alongside the vessel [HMS *Beagle*], and remained there out of mere curiosity, whilst the sleet fell and thawed on her naked bosom, and the skin of her naked baby!"

The Yakuts have been strongly influenced by Russian settlement in the north. Today, many of them work in industry and various trades, and many work on collective farms, in the Yakut ASSR (Yakut Autonomous Soviet Socialist Republic). The coldest place in the Northern Hemisphere, Verkhoyansk, lies near the center of this province. Its average temperature in January is -59°F.

West of the Tungus and Yakuts lies the land of the Samoyeds, and beyond them live the Lapps. The Lapp territory stretches from northwest Russia's Kola Peninsula (whose chief city is the famous World War II port of Murmansk) to northern Norway. But most Lapps live in northern Scandinavia, particularly Norway, where many are fishermen or have settled down as farmers. Some, however, have carried the domestication of reindeer to its highest development, and thus made the Arctic's longest native advance along mankind's path from the hunting Middle Stone Age to the agricultural New Stone Age. Reindeer herding also introduced the idea of capitalism, or at least of personal wealth and hired labor, to the Arctic.

THE way in which men first learned to tame wild cattle, horses and other animals is lost in the mists of prehistory. One clue may lie in the seasonal migrations of the reindeer. It is conceivable that a band of hunters following a particular herd throughout the year would come to regard it in time as their personal property. If so, they would protect the herd from predators and from other hunters, and try to control its movements. Eventually, the animals would become familiar with the men and would allow fairly close contact. This is essentially the method employed in very recent times by some tribes of the Siberian Arctic. A few of the tribes use dogs to assist in herding. The semidomesticated reindeer are sometimes harnessed to sledges, but more often, it is the dogs that pull the sledge.

The more advanced method of reindeer herding, employed by the Lapps and some others, may well be an adaptation of the techniques of horse herding learned on the steppes of central Asia. The use of dogs to assist the herders and of lassos to capture the animals, the practices of strapping baggage to their backs and even riding on them—all these could easily have been transferred from one economy to the other.

When mention of Lapps first begins to occur in western literature, they are usually described as reindeer hunters; references to them as herders are very few. During the past 500 years, however, the reindeer-herding Lapp of the inland plateaus has become well known. The way of life of the reindeer Lapp is determined by the instinctive seasonal rhythms and needs of his animals. The seasonal rhythms of the tame reindeer are those of the wild caribou. During the winter the Lapp lets his herd shelter deep in the inland plateau or in a forest where shallower snow makes it easier for them

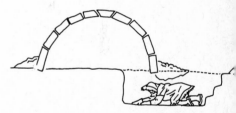

ENTRY TO AN IGLOO is by a passage tunneled under the snow. Such a corridor has two advantages for the Eskimo trying to maintain a warm shelter:

● First, because it is down out of the wind, and cold air cannot blow into the igloo. When a sunken entry cannot be built because of a light snow cover, an above-ground entry hall of snow blocks is built. It should be placed on the side of the igloo away from the direction of the prevailing winds.

● Second, because a tunnel entry allows warm air, which is lighter than cold air, to collect inside the dome. Eskimos often live seminude in an igloo heated to 60° or more by their body heat or by a small oil cooking lamp. A hole must be kept open in the igloo for ventilation and to keep the inside wall from melting.

to get at lichens. In spring comes the drive to fresh pastures and calving grounds. Traditionally the entire Lapp family accompanied the herd, with its baggage tied on the animals' backs or on reindeer-drawn sledges. A few weeks after calving, the reindeer are ready either to go into the high mountains or to swim across to the offshore islands to spend the summer growing fat on the plentiful grass and lichens. In midsummer the Lapps round up the reindeer to count them, cut notches in their ears as personal brands, and to castrate many of the male calves. The animals are then released until autumn, when they swim back to the mainland or descend to the lowlands. In September they are once again ushered into corrals for the annual sorting and slaughter. After that, they return to their winter pastures.

WHAT the yak is to the Tibetan and the llama to the Peruvian, the reindeer formerly was to the Lapp, an all-purpose animal. He prefers its meat boiled or smoked, and particularly relishes reindeer broth. He now keeps goats for milk, but in the past he milked reindeer cows. The half-cup of very rich and chalky milk that each gave was regarded as a special treat either drunk or made into cheese. From reindeer skin the Lapp makes all of his heavy winter clothing except his cloth hat. In former times he also made his summer clothes of it, often with the hair scraped off. Today, everything but the leather leggings is made from gaily decorated cloth.

For transportation, the Lapp uses his reindeer both as a burden-bearer and sledge-puller. His sledges are of two types. The one used on the open tundra resembles a sleigh and is both high and wide. The type used in the forest resembles the front half of a canoe and requires expert balance on the part of the rider. This little sleigh, or pulka, is hitched to the reindeer by means of a single leather thong which passes between its legs and fastens to a neck yoke. The animal is steered by means of a single rein tied to the left antler. When going downhill, the pulka will often catch up to the reindeer and run into its back legs, sending both beast and passenger rolling in the snow.

The invention of the ski, the highest development of the snowshoe, is regarded as a noteworthy Lapp contribution to southern civilization. Until sport skiing became popular in the latter part of the 19th Century, the ski was a purely utilitarian device for winter travel. Remains found in the Scandinavian bogs indicate that the Lapps were using skis 3,000 years ago. The ski is of great importance to the Lapp in winter reindeer herding.

Intermarriage with Norwegians, Finns, Swedes and Russians is common and is destroying whatever traces remain of a distinctive Lapp physical stock. Although they have traditionally been described as dwarfs with oriental features, uncostumed Lapps in northern Scandinavia are all but indistinguishable from their neighbors. Their "oriental" features in most cases seem to be a product of imagination, and those with high cheekbones look no more oriental than do the Highlanders of Scotland. Because the section of the Arctic in which they live is next door to people of European culture, the Lapps' way of life is rapidly disappearing. Most women and children no longer accompany the migration with the herds. Even the features of animal management have been radically modified, and modern slaughter and freezing plants are appearing on the tundra. Attendance at schools is weaning young Lapps away from the nomadic reindeer life. Now they often go off into other trades and professions, and the shortage of

POISED SPEARMAN

WIDE-EYED CARIBOU

STONE SCULPTURES by Eskimo artists, shown above and on the opposite page, are carved of soapstone. Granite, bone and walrus ivory are also worked. The tallest of these four figures, the spearman, is only seven and a half inches high.

herders in some areas has made it necessary to form reindeer cooperatives.

Some, and likely all, the arctic peoples of North America crossed the Bering Strait from Asia, either by land bridge, ice or water. These peoples —Aleuts, Indians and Eskimos—probably arrived after the majority of Indians who continued southward. The Aleuts are a Paleo-Asiatic group who moved down the shores of Alaska and settled in the Aleutian Islands. They have been all but wiped out by disease, by Russian fur traders in the 18th and 19th Centuries, and by the Japanese who invaded the Aleutians in World War II.

The Indians long-settled in northeast Canada are the Little Whale River Indians and the Naskapi of the Ungava region. The former River Indians, who have traditionally lived by hunting and trapping caribou, have been forced by the scarcity of these animals to move toward Hudson Bay, where they can capture stranded white whales. The Naskapi, or Nenenot Indians, are a small hunting group noted for their remarkable ability to carry on conversations over distances as great as two miles in high, penetrating voices. In the forests of northwestern Canada and the interior of Alaska live the Athabaskans, who are related to the Navajos of the southwestern United States. Originally these people hunted and fished along the rivers and lakes and lived in nonpermanent villages. Now the advance of white civilization is forcing them into new ways of life.

MOTHER AND CHILD

No one really knows where the Eskimos came from. It is widely believed that they are descended from a group of hunting and fishing people who entered North America about 5,000 years ago. Archaeologists have discovered that some of the carvings and religious and ceremonial practices of these people were much the same as those of certain Siberian tribes. This has led to the belief that the ancestors of the Eskimos originated in the interior of Siberia.

An interesting new theory about the source of Eskimo culture has recently been advanced by a Soviet anthropologist. After an examination of tools, hunting gear and primitive art excavated on northeastern Siberia's Chukchi Peninsula, where some Eskimos settled and still live, S. I. Rudenko concluded that they had come from the South Sea Islands, particularly Melanesia. The islanders, he believes, worked their way up through the island chains fringing East Asia to Kamchatka and the coasts and islands of the Bering Sea. According to this theory the skills of seamanship, boat building and harpooning that are possessed by the South Sea Islanders were the only ones that could have insured the survival of sea mammal hunters in the Bering Sea region. Rudenko also noted that the elaborate ornamentation skillfully etched on the bone and ivory implements of the Bering Sea people resembles the ancient pottery of the islands and certain scrollwork found in Melanesia.

Whatever their origin, it is known that Eskimos migrated from northern Alaska to the Canadian Arctic some 800 to 1,000 years ago. When they reached the shores of the Atlantic, one group went south along the Labrador coast, another to Greenland.

Most Greenland Eskimos, except those living around Thule in the northwest, have become heavily mixed over the centuries with European settlers. Today most of them have European blood, both by descent from the old Norsemen and by intermarriage with later immigrants, chiefly the

LOWERING MUSK OX

AN ANCIENT ART, Eskimo carving has been practiced for thousands of years among various tribes. These objects are from Baffin Island, those opposite from Hudson Bay. Canada encourages the best artists and sponsors sale of their work.

Danes. On the whole, the people have changed so much in appearance and culture that they are no longer known as Eskimos, but simply as Greenlanders, or *Kalâtdlit* in Greenlandic.

All living Eskimos—some 55,000 of them—would not fill a major football stadium. Outside Greenland, the two largest populations live along the coastal regions of Alaska and Labrador. There are some 18,000 in Alaska and the islands in the Bering Sea, but in all the Canadian Arctic only about 10,000. Where Eskimos and Indians are close neighbors, they look much alike, undoubtedly due to intermixing. Generally, Eskimos differ from Indians in having higher, broader cheekbones; small, flat or narrow noses, and often, slanting eyes. Mongolian in appearance, they are short and stocky with straight black hair and brownish skin. Their babies are born with the blue Mongolian spot at the base of the spine.

SINCE they live in great hardship and discomfort, with death by violent accident or starvation always near, one would expect Eskimos to be grim if not despairing. On the contrary, they have long appeared to be among the world's happiest people—cheerful, generous, friendly, good-natured, and more given to gaiety and laughter than many primitive tribes in tropical countries. Traditional Eskimo society is—in the early Christian rather than the Marxist sense—communistic. Eskimos own their private kits of weapons, utensils and clothing. Otherwise they believe that the resources of nature belong to everyone, and are to be shared not only with members of their own community but with any passing strangers. The male Eskimo's highest ambition is not to get rich, but to become a good hunter and provider, a good contributor to his community. The worst punishment he can suffer—inflicted only for such grave crimes as murder—is to be ostracized by his community. Within it he feels securely wanted, needed, appreciated, and sure that in time of sickness or accident or bad hunting he and his family will get all the help that the community can give.

An Eskimo's house is always open to others for as long as they wish or need to stay, and his favorite pastime is visiting neighbors and relatives. When he has had a good hunt, he will call out to the whole village: "Come visit my house!" The guests come in flocks, for a high old time of gorging, singing, dancing and storytelling. If the host's provisions run out, another hunter will invite everyone to come on to his house. Moving from house to house, the party may last for days.

The Eskimos do not fear death. They regard it as either an end to everything or a transition to something new and better. Old people who could no longer hunt or otherwise contribute to community life used to kill themselves because they felt there was nothing left to live for. This was sometimes done, with help, at the height of a party, when everyone including the one about to die was having a good time.

Eskimos are famous for their practice of exchanging or lending wives, and for parties at which the light is put out and mates are exchanged indiscriminately. Vilhjalmur Stefansson has explained this in part by his finding that—like ancient men who believed that women were made pregnant by the wind or by bathing in a certain stream—at least some Eskimos apparently do not understand the facts of life.

In any event, any child born to a woman is precious to her husband. The Eskimo's child is perhaps the world's most pampered, petted and

ESKIMO INNER CLOTHING will keep a man warm in all but the coldest weather if he is moderately active. The outfit above weighs only about six pounds.

● The tunic, made from a soft fur or even from bird skins, has the hair or feathers inside, providing an air space in which the warm air from the body collects. Nonporous material, tightly sewn seams, the absence of buttonholes and a snug fit across the shoulders keep the heat in.

● Pants are made from such heavy, longwearing pelts as polar bear or caribou. They extend only just below the top of the boots, into which they are loosely tucked.

● Footwear is variable. Usually a "sock" is worn, with the fur side inward; it is loose-fitting and is packed with dry grass which is changed frequently. A slipper-like low boot may be worn over the sock.

indulged. Various explanations have been offered. Many Eskimo babies die in infancy, and those that survive are accordingly treasured. The child is regarded by its parents as social security for their old age. It is thought to be inhabited by the spirit of the wise and heroic ancestor for whom it has been named, and that spirit must not be offended. There remains the possibility that Eskimos may simply love children. Far from being spoiled, Eskimo children grow up with the sense of warm security within their community, and are introduced early to their stern responsibilities to that community in its unending struggle for survival. Except for the aged, who are honored in good times but used to be left out to die when food was scarce and the survival of the family or community was at stake, the Eskimos have no leisure class.

The life is hard and precarious at best, but ingenuity has made it less so than might seem possible. No one has better applied the fact that warm air cannot escape downward. Early explorers and other white men who ventured into the Arctic sealed themselves inside several layers of heavy clothing. The result was not only awkward bulkiness but perilous, sweat-soaked chill. They soon learned to imitate the Eskimo's loose-fitting parka, which lets his body heat circulate freely and escape only when the Eskimo grows too warm and pulls his parka hood loose at the neck.

The same principle is applied in the building of Eskimo winter houses, usually made of earth or sometimes of earth-packed stone. The house is heated only by blubber lamps and body heat. But it stays warm because the tunnel entrance is lower than the raised sitting and sleeping space.

"Igloo" is an Eskimo word that means "snowhouse" to outsiders but to the Eskimo means simply "house." Three fourths of all Eskimos have never even seen a snowhouse. Only the Canadian arctic Eskimos ever live in one more than a few days. The rest use them only when traveling. An Eskimo can build one in 30 to 60 minutes, and keeps it warm by the same method used in his regular home.

SIMILAR ingenuity appears in Eskimo hunting. Because dead seals tend to sink in summer, for example, he makes a harpoon with a detachable head connected by a line to an inflated sealskin. In winter, seals surface under small breathing holes in the ice. The Eskimo inserts a stick into the hole in such a way that the seal must touch the stick with its nose when it comes to breathe. With his harpoon in hand, the Eskimo will wait for hours. When he sees the stick move, he thrusts home.

Few Eskimos swim, yet in maneuvering a kayak they show no fear of the water and are able to capsize the lightweight boat, right it with the thrust of a paddle, and perform other dexterous stunts. To bring down birds, they throw the bolas, a set of balls attached to strings, which the hunter swings around his head lasso-fashion and lets fly toward an oncoming flock.

All these skills and customs were part of the Eskimo's way of life for centuries. They have not yet vanished, but with the coming of the white man, Eskimo life began to change. Much has been written about the distressing aspects of that change: the white trader's creation of new wants; the Eskimo's shift from hunting to fur trapping in order to satisfy those wants; his bewilderment and discontent at his loss of buying power when white fox became unfashionable and synthetic furs appeared; his lack of resistance to such exotic diseases as measles and whooping cough which for

ESKIMO OUTER CLOTHING is added to inner wear in extreme cold or during periods of inactivity such as waiting at a seal's breathing hole. Outerwear weighs about four pounds, so the complete costume comes to 10 pounds, compared to the 20 or 30 pounds of cold-weather garb worn by a European or American.

● The outer tunic is worn with the hair out. A strip of wolverine or wolf fur goes around the hoods of both tunics because, unlike other furs, it does not collect ice frozen from the moisture of the breath.

● Roomy mittens extend to the sleeves. The tunic is designed so that one's arms can be pulled inside to warm the hands.

● High boots with fur outside may be worn over the long socks (opposite page). Several pairs of boots may be worn, one over the other, in very cold weather.

a time proved deadly to him; his confusion and dismay when missionaries denounced his religious beliefs and customs; his resentment when the white policeman and administrator punished him for following ancient custom, and his loss of initiative when they treated him as a child. But the new and better trend in Eskimo-white relations is much less widely known.

In many jobs in the Arctic, the Eskimo would be superior to the white man, but he needs training before he can work as anything but a laborer. Many companies in the Canadian north now realize this and provide on-the-job training and special vocational courses. One oil company is training Eskimos as drillers in order to solve the problem of finding experienced men who will stay on the rigs. A school has been established to teach geology to Eskimos who will become prospectors. The Canadian government is encouraging native art, trying to organize the gathering of eider down (a superb insulating material for clothing and sleeping bags) and experimenting with such materials as foam plastic blocks for better igloos. There are dozens of such projects to improve the Eskimo's standard of living and to restore his initiative. One excellent device to the latter end is the local or regional Eskimo council, in which Eskimos gather to consider and manage their own affairs. Recently the Eskimo Council in Alaska called upon Congress to define clearly their hunting, fishing and land rights.

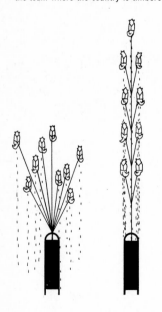

A SLEDGE HARNESS of walrus hide or sealskin fits on a dog's chest and fore-quarters, as shown above, and lets the dog pull without interfering with its legs. A fan hitch for a dog team, drawn at bottom left, is best for fast travel in open country. The feather hitch, at bottom right, permits more precise driving of the team where the country is timbered.

WHAT is being attempted in Canada and to a small extent in the United States has already been accomplished in Greenland. For self-government, all Greenlanders over 23 now elect a National Council and Local Councils. The latter provide assistance to widows and orphans, and to the aged and disabled, who were often allowed to perish in the old culture. Medical care, medicines and hospitalization are free. Education is free and compulsory to age 14; literacy is universal. In 1953 Greenland was made an equal and integral part of Denmark.

What happened in Greenland to bring this about is now happening in most of the Arctic. Whites and natives are mixing and changing. In general, both groups have begun to dress alike: native dress for winter, immigrant dress for summer. New settlers have taken to snowshoes and dog sleds, Eskimos have taken to wooden canoes and begun to propel their big skin umiaks with outboard motors.

Eskimos and Indians have become American military pilots and riflemen. Norwegians in Kirkenes saw the German army driven out by Samoyed soldiers of the Russian army riding reindeer. Lapps in Norway publish their own newspaper, and the Athabaskans at Fort Yukon have formed a jazz band that practices by playing along with radio broadcasts.

By now, the intermixing between aborigines and immigrants is almost complete in some areas. There is a tendency toward a single blended population extending over the entire Arctic. Like the original arctic people, this new breed loves the harsh land. To them, it is as strong as the rugged, snow-capped mountains, as beautiful as the midnight sun on an isolated tundra lake. They pity people who never see the brilliant northern lights, or the great migrations of caribou herds. They have adapted to the strenuous requirements of the Arctic, and the struggle for existence has toughened their bodies and developed their minds. They are a hardy, independent people with a remarkable spiritual and material culture, and they are certain to play major roles in the coming arctic boom.

A TEAM OF YELPING HUSKIES FANS OUT WIDE OVER THE SNOW TO HAUL AN ESKIMO SLED ON A BAFFIN ISLAND SEAL-HUNTING TRIP

Peoples of the Arctic

For reasons most men cannot comprehend, small bands of people persist in dwelling amid the Arctic's rigors. Over thousands of years, hunters like the Eskimos have adapted the lore of the chase to killing the big game of far-north waters, while others, like the Lapps, have turned their skills to taming the reindeer. Each people in its way has fought the Arctic to a draw.

The Enduring Eskimo

A FARSEEING HUNTER, a Pond Inlet Eskimo proudly holds up his old brass telescope, which cuts down enormously the time he spends roaming the sea ice for signs of seals.

The last of the Mongoloid peoples to reach North America, the Eskimos were left with the least of the pickings. For 5,000 years the Arctic has been their domain, the sea mammals of the icebound coasts and the caribou of the tundra their principal bounty. Today about 55,000 Eskimos survive, strung in a thinly manned line from the Bering Strait to the western shores of Greenland. Army tents, rifles and telescopes are now useful parts of the Eskimo hunter's equipment, but his life still turns on its ancient objective: to kill enough seals the year round to ward off starvation. Hardheaded realists, Eskimos, like the Pond Inlet people shown on these pages, have taken from the white man only what they could put to good use. About arctic survival, they have little to learn from anyone else.

AN ESKIMO FAMILY BUILDS A TRUNCATED IGLOO ON ICE-COVERED ECLIPSE SOUND. IT IS SPRING AND A SNOW ROOF WOULD MELT,

MODERNIZED CAMP for a Pond Inlet family is pitched on a firm bed of gravel away from ground made mushy by the summer thaw. In the warm months Army tents replace the traditional sod huts or skin tents, and cloth garments are worn instead of furs, an imported solution to the once-pressing Eskimo problem of keeping cool in hot weather.

SO THEY USE CANVAS FOR ROOFING. WITH SAWS TO CUT THE HUGE BLOCKS, THEY CAN PUT UP A SNUG SHELTER IN 40 MINUTES

POISED TO KILL, a Pond Inlet Eskimo (*left*) stands stock-still by a mound of ice that marks a seal's breathing hole. He has to shoot fast when a seal noses to the surface, then stab it with a harpoon.

USING NETS, an Eskimo traps seals where gaps show in the winter ice (*opposite*). The nets are laid underwater and held by guy ropes. A seal tangled in one will drown or be clubbed to death.

STALKING a seal as it cat-naps in the sun (*below*), a hunter moves in for the kill behind a screen. One misstep and the quarry he has been stalking for hours will slither down a hole in the ice.

The Life-and-Death Search for Seals

Pond Inlet lies at the northern end of Baffin Island, and the Eskimo families that live along its rim rarely venture inland. The frozen sea is their highway, their hunting ground and often their campsite as well. Only in August does the sea lap against an ice-free shore. The rest of the year, the ice dictates the terms for the hunt. In winter when it is thick, hunters must keep vigils over the breathing holes of seals (*above*) or go through the bone-chilling labor of setting nets in cold waters (*opposite, top*). Sometimes this is fruitless, and families have starved to death in the winter. In spring and summer, when the seals come out to bask in the sun, the hunt is plentiful. Even then, until a man learns how to move unnoticed over slushy ice fields (*right*) the seals can easily escape him.

A Partnership for Survival

Without their dog teams, Eskimos could not stay alive. On foot, no hunter could cover enough territory to keep his family in food. But a team of dogs hitched to a sled can carry him over the ice at speeds up to 20 miles an hour. Pushed hard, teams have been driven for 18 hours at a stretch. The famed Husky sled dog is one of four much-interbred arctic types. All are descended from Asiatic species, including the tough little Siberian Husky on these pages. All lead a hard life; the Eskimo never pampers them. The sled dogs double as partners in the hunt: set free of their traces, they will nose out half-hidden seal holes and bring polar bears to bay (*below*). The dogs are not an unmixed blessing. The Eskimo must spend half his time hunting just to feed the voracious appetite of his indispensable ally.

A SOAKING DOG is hauled out of the water by an Eskimo after swimming across a gap in the ice. Entire teams often are drowned when cracks appear suddenly in the sea ice.

SNARLING DOGS circle a polar bear, which wheels warily to fend them off. When a dog team scents a bear, the Eskimo driver slashes the traces and the dogs streak off to chase it. Nipping fiercely at the polar bear's haunches, often at the cost of their lives, the dogs will hold the bear at bay long enough for the hunter to arrive on foot and shoot it.

SLEEPING DOGS of an Eskimo's team lie curled up in the drifting snow. Their thick fur insulates their bodies so well that they can sleep in the snow even when the temperature drops to 70° below zero. They are hitched to the sled by individual harnesses made of walrus skin. If they are not fed enough seal meat the dogs will eat up the trace lines.

IN NORWAY, A LAPP WOMAN AND CHILD WEAR EMBROIDERED CAPS TO CHURCH

The Archaic Lapp

High in northern Scandinavia live Europe's last surviving aborigines, the Lapps. Related neither to the Mongoloid nor to the modern European races, they are the remnant of ancient people who inhabited Europe before those racial stocks evolved. Hunters of the reindeer, the forebears of the Lapps followed the herds north as the ice-age glaciers receded. Today 35,000 Lapps share the forests and the tundra with nearly 500,000 reindeer. Some Lapps, living in forests, still rely almost as heavily on hunting small game as they do on their half-tamed herds. Others live as fishermen and farmers on the rocky Atlantic and arctic coasts. Only in isolated parts of Lapland can the true Lapp herdsmen be found—following their reindeer from winter retreats to summer pasturage. Lapps are short, well-muscled people; most of them are swarthy, but some bear the fair imprint of intermarriage with blond Scandinavians. Recently given the chance to trade and settle in log cabins, they have taken it up eagerly. But they still cast their lot with their herds and their life remains an arduous one.

A FORLORN VILLAGE of Finnish Lapps is whipped by a winter storm (*right*). In recent years many Lapps have turned from nomadism to rude permanent settlements like this.

DRIVING A HERD across a coastal strait, Lapps on shore wave and shout to urge the laggards on while men in rowboats try to head the leaders in the right direction. The herdsmen's work is strenuous because reindeer are easily frightened and much less docile than cattle. The rear animals of a reindeer herd must be constantly pushed into line.

A Culture Harnessed to the Reindeer

Until lately most reindeer Lapps lived their whole lives on the trail, camping in tents and moving on whenever the reindeer moved. They formed closely knit, self-sufficient units—a few Lapp families and their meat on the hoof, wandering a well-established course as the seasons changed. The reindeer still migrate but the Lapps no longer follow quite so closely on their heels. In the winter when the herds retreat to the forests, they are left loosely guarded by herdsmen. For most of the year, the herders' families are left behind in permanent villages. Only at winter's end do many of the Lapps leave home to drive the herds to summer pasturage. At that time the snow is heavily crusted in the forest and the reindeer can no longer paw the ground clear to find lichens. They must be driven up the mountain slopes beyond timber line or down to the coasts and offshore islands, where the snow is soft and thaws early, and the lichens are fresh. This summer drive is the Lapps' last solid link to their passing nomadic life. They still depend on the reindeer for their staple food, much of their clothing and most of their barter. But the old crafts of the herdsman, tent-maker and sledge driver, are now in the hands of specialists.

SCRAMBLING ASHORE on their summer island (*right*), the reindeer unlimber after their cold swim. In the foreground a Lapp woman helps an exhausted fawn over the rocks,

TAKING TO WATER, reindeer swim for an island off the coast of Norway for summer pasture. Confined to the island by their strong dislike for swimming great distances, the reindeer are safely left to roam at will. There they will feed on lichens and grasses until the onset of autumn, when the herdsmen will drive them back inland to the pine forests.

Autumn Roundup in Lapland

In the autumn the work of the Lapp herdsmen comes to fruition. Before the rutting season begins hundreds of reindeer are rounded up in big corrals for the yearly slaughter and sorting-out of herds. For the kill, the sick and the maimed are chosen first, then the superfluous bulls. The healthiest bulls—and all the does—are left to breed. A single family will slaughter a fifth of its reindeer each year, drying and storing the meat for its food supply. Although Lapp women still make boots, coats and trousers from reindeer hide, most of the skins are set aside for trading, since the Lapp economy is increasingly directed to the big winter trade fairs held in villages in the south of Lapland. As customers for everything from coffee to sewing machines, the Lapps are steadily being drawn into the Scandinavian economy. Their reindeer, which they followed north thousands of years ago, are rapidly becoming a source of cash instead of the basis of all existence.

SCRAPING SKINS, a band of Lapps keeps warm beside a fire built under an oil drum. The freshly cut reindeer skins, legs still attached, are heaped up to be stretched and dried.

MILLING IN A CORRAL, reindeer charge dangerously close to a herder (*opposite*) as he waits for a chance to lasso one by its antlers. Ear markings identify each family's stock.

AN ICE TUNNEL 1,100 feet long
is used by the U.S. Army to measure the ice flow within the vast
Greenland icecap 18 miles from
Thule. Along the walls are power
lines and a large ventilation pipe.

7

The Coming Boom in the Arctic

MAN started out as a semitropical organism and still is one: his body feels most at home when the temperature is about 85°. His first civilizations emerged somewhat north of the equator in the warm latitudes of the Mediterranean and the Middle East. But because most of the earth's land lies in the Northern Hemisphere, his progress since then has been steadily northward—that is, poleward. Of late this movement has accelerated, and at the present point in history massive human forces are converging on the strategic Arctic. World population is expanding at a record rate, and the north is the one big empty place near its main centers. World trade and travel are taking to the skies, and the north is their great short cut. World power has passed to the continent-sized nations rimming the Arctic, and the north is the frontier they must man and maintain.

The Russians are busily unlocking a "jewel chest" of Siberian mineral wealth, the Canadians are preparing to develop their vast north country as "the great tomorrow land" and the United States has extended its northern boundary into the Arctic Circle by adding Alaska as its 49th and largest state. Population, technology, military needs—these are the dynamics that are thrusting civilization farther north, and they seem to spring from man's own nature and destiny. Yet there may also be a deeper factor at work, one which may already have speeded these developments. This is the warming trend in the climate of the north that has been going on for at least half a century, a slow but seemingly sure change that many people who live in the Northern Hemisphere can confirm with observations from their own surroundings. All reliable meteorological data show an upward movement in temperatures over the past several decades: in Norway, average temperatures have risen by 2° since 1930. Nearly all the great glaciers of the hemisphere are in leisurely retreat and it is estimated that the huge Greenland ice sheet is showing a net loss of about 22 cubic miles of ice every year.

The question is whether the warm-up is a long-term trend or only temporary, and the answer at the moment is that nobody knows. But "if this trend continues for another half century," says Canada's J. Tuzo Wilson, president of the International Union of Geodesy and Geophysics during the IGY, "the results will be spectacular." At the very least it may be expected that navigation in the ice-choked polar seas should become easier, and that polar routes will become more useful to mankind.

However this warm-up question is settled, it is already clear that the ancient barriers of cold, ice and polar darkness no longer will be allowed to stand in man's way. He has moved all the paraphernalia of his bustling civilization into Fairbanks, Alaska, including antifreeze in the fire hydrants. He is pressing north into the Canadian tundra, despite the mosquitoes. In Soviet Russia young people are being mobilized in a new, 500,000-member pioneer force "to turn barren stretches of northern and eastern Siberia into a new industrial empire."

Because so much Soviet land and resources lie so far north, the Russians have taken the lead in opening up their northlands. They started systematic development of their northern regions 20 years before the Canadians and the Americans. By 1958, when there were 30,000 people living in the Canadian Arctic, the population of the Soviet north was about four and a half million. Nearly two thirds of this earlier pioneer force had settled there within the preceding 35 years. The population of the United States north of the Arctic Circle today is less than 10,000, of Danish-administered Greenland less than 5,000. In 1960, when the largest New World settlement north of the Arctic Circle was the Alaskan hamlet of Barrow (1,314 permanent residents), four Soviet arctic cities counted 50,000 inhabitants or more. The largest of these is Murmansk (famous as the arctic sea delivery port for Allied aid to Russia in World War II), which now has a population of 226,000. The fastest growing is the city of Norilsk, located in north-central Siberia at the same latitude as Point Barrow, the northern tip of Alaska. Little more than a trading post in 1940, Norilsk turned into a boom town when copper, nickel, gold, cobalt and coal were discovered nearby, and today is a city of 108,000 with one of the world's most northerly television stations, a concert hall, schools, nurseries and blocks of apartment houses.

Of most immediate importance today in drawing men northward are the military requirements of the Arctic. An estimated one out of three persons now living in Alaska is a member or dependent of the armed forces.

The military is in the forefront of all exploration and research in the Arctic. Even the peopling of the north is of some military concern, because if the Arctic should ever become a theater of war, the presence of a settled population that knew the north and how to exist there would be of great importance to the survival of fighting forces. Both American and Soviet air forces make frequent surveillance flights over the pole; and American and Soviet airmen and scientists have operated airstrips on the so-called "T-islands" when these huge floating ice-islands have drifted to one side or the other of the North Polar Basin. In the 1950s the United States and Canada jointly set up a ring of Arctic-circling radar stations to provide early warning against a transpolar bombing attack. Because Soviet rockets are making this network obsolescent, they are adding a longer-range Ballistic Missile Early Warning System.

A major outpost in this defense arc is Thule, 950 miles from the pole on the icy northwest coast of Greenland. To detect ICBMs while they are still ascending, two powerful radar beams fan northward over the Arctic from four antennae, each the size of a 30-story building. Thule is the United States Air Force's northernmost base, with a 14,000-foot ice runway and a complement of more than 6,000 men. Its radar installation is matched at the west end of the BMEWS line by an equally massive station at Clear, Alaska. The Soviet Union has not only built its own network of air bases, missile bases and radar stations along its arctic frontier, but has also carried out nuclear testing at such far northern sites as Novaya Zemlya and the Kolguyev islands. All of these advanced bases require elaborate supply lines from the south: supplying the Distant Early Warning line above the Arctic Circle takes 45,000 tons of cargo a year, delivered by air, tankers, LSTs and barges. The whole logistic effort is giving the peoples of more temperate latitudes a tremendous amount of know-how about living and working in the once-unknown Arctic.

O F all the possibilities that are being examined in the north for man's future, probably the first to be exploited will be its mineral resources. The Russians are showing the way in Siberia, and much of Europe's high-quality steel already comes from the big Swedish iron mines at Kiruna, north of the Arctic Circle. The New World too may soon be tapping its northern wealth as never before. United States Steel and other big corporations are turning to the iron ores of the Canadian shield as the nearest available rich and dependable source of the most vitally important of all industrial raw materials. Before long much of the steel produced in the United States may be made from iron ore brought from the Canadian north. Already huge mines have been opened in Labrador and northern Quebec, and others will eventually be linked by rail with an ocean port at Ungava Bay. Geologists have meanwhile established the existence of more iron deposits still farther north on Baffin Island.

Similarly the fastest growing branch of Soviet heavy industry is located in central Siberia, where big steel mills have been built since World War II to tap the iron ores of Tashtagol and Novokuznetsk (Stalinsk until November 1961). Rich deposits of copper, nickel and uranium are also being developed in the Soviet and Canadian Arctic. By energetic exploitation of the gold fields of Magadan in northeast Siberia the Soviet Union has made itself into one of the world's foremost gold producers. In the current

THE PERMAFROST PROBLEM and solutions to it are shown in these diagrams. The building above, erected on top of the frozen soil, was destroyed by thaw. Heat passing through the floor melted the soil; the structure sank into the mud.

SAFELY ELEVATED, this shed is constructed atop an open wooden cribbing, which allows cold air to circulate under the floor. As a further precaution against the permafrost's melting, the foundation is placed on top of a mound of gravel.

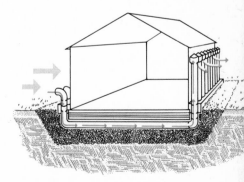

SAFELY INSULATED by refrigeration, this large building allows little heat to leak into the frost. Cold wind (indicated by arrows) blows through metal ducts laid in a bed of gravel and keeps the ground under the building from melting.

Seven Year Plan, the Siberian Yakut republic is expected to increase the Soviet diamond output almost twentyfold by 1965. The Communist diamond capital of Mirny, which was a rude Siberian tent camp in the mid-1950s when the diamond-rich "Peace Pipe" formation was discovered nearby, already has a population of 20,000 people.

The north promises to become a rich source of oil for the world. The United States Navy has taken rights to a huge oil and gas field under the permafrost south of Point Barrow. American firms have budgeted $300 million for Alaskan oil-prospecting in the 1960s. Besides exploiting three new northern fields, the Russians are increasing Siberian geological prospecting under the Seven Year Plan by 300 to 400 per cent. Some of the world's biggest oil deposits are believed to exist in the Canadian north. Reserves in the Mackenzie valley and northern Yukon alone are estimated at a hundred billion barrels. Still farther north an oil rush is sweeping over the Canadian arctic islands, where a drilling team struck oil in 1961 only 900 miles from the pole, on Melville Island. Geologists say there may be 30 billion barrels of oil under these islands.

The twin keys to the development of all such northern resources are transport and power. To supply power for the heavy industry built on the ore fields and bauxite deposits of Siberia, the Soviet Union is building a power station at Bratsk on the Angara River that will be nearly twice as big as Grand Coulee, biggest in the United States, and is planning another, still bigger one at Krasnoyarsk on the Yenisey. Alaska has plans for a Yukon River dam at Rampart Canyon that would have two-and-a-half times the installed capacity (two million kilowatts) of Grand Coulee. Nuclear energy, as well as hydroelectric power, is destined for a big role in the arctic future. The United States Army already has installed two 1,500-kilowatt reactors to provide power at bases in Greenland and Alaska, and is experimenting with small, trailer-mounted mobile reactors that can be airlifted in two planeloads and put to work within 12 hours of delivery. Such portable units could provide the necessary energy for mining, oil and industrial ventures in remote places.

WHEN it comes to transport, the Arctic is a world of few roads and almost no railroads. The Alaska Highway, built as a defense measure to link western Canada and the United States with Fairbanks, 1,500 miles northwest of Dawson Creek, has played a big part in Alaska's post-World War II advance. Yet the building and maintaining of this famous road points up the particularly frustrating problem of the permafrost. In summer thaws, stretches of the highway itself are likely to slide about atop the frozen ground, and cars and trucks quickly become mired in the spongy mud if they leave the gravel highway. This muskeg, as Canadians call the smelly muck atop the permafrost, has sucked down roads, animals, trucks and even landing strips.

It is no wonder that to keep from getting bogged down, Canadians, Americans and Russians alike have leapfrogged over the muskeg straight into the air age. Bush pilots haul cargoes everywhere in Alaska and Canada, and the Soviet press tells of turboprop planes flying daily from Moscow to the farthest corners of the Arctic. Such local airlines are also being linked to the dramatic new routes of transpolar air travel. Already Thule in Greenland, Coral Harbour and Frobisher Bay in northern Canada are among the emergency landing fields for the airline jets that nightly wing their way across the North Pole short cut between Scandinavia and the Pacific coast. All such bases as well as the advanced military bases in the north must be supplied at least partly by surface vessels. The Soviet Northern Sea Route Administration keeps a half dozen icebreakers and some 20 cargo ships plying the arctic coast supply line between Murmansk in the west and Vladivostok some 6,000 miles to the east. To bring Canadian arctic oil to market, Canada's Deputy Minister of Northern Affairs has suggested an underwater pipeline from the arctic islands to an ice-free port in western Greenland.

THE day is drawing near, as planes get ever bigger and faster, when passengers and cargo will ride in rockets, and when world transport will be revolutionized. Sea as well as air transport will be shaken up by the revolution. In crossing the top of the world under the polar ice in 1959, the nuclear submarines *Nautilus* and *Skate* pioneered what may become a route for commercial cargoes. Giant 20,000- to 40,000-ton nuclear submarine tankers blueprinted for the United States Maritime Administration could shorten sea trips by thousands of miles by taking the arctic short cut. (Sample savings: Tokyo to London, from 11,200 to 6,500 miles; Seattle to Oslo, from 9,300 to 6,100 miles.) *Nautilus* skipper William Anderson suggests that Barrow, Alaska, may have a long-range future as a point of departure for transpolar submarine traffic. The Barrow Submarine Canyon lies just offshore, a deepwater channel that Commander Anderson found is the best corridor into the Arctic Basin through the shallow Bering Strait.

Beneath the surface of the northern seas, still another rich resource lies waiting for man to exploit it. This is the marine life of the Arctic, which promises to add significantly to the world's food supply. In the open waters along the fringe of arctic ice, mineral nutrients from the deep nourish a tremendous supply of the drifting plankton life on which fish, shrimp and other, larger sea creatures feed. The warmer trend in world temperatures has begun to lure more fish northward, and the fishing fleets are following after. Herring and haddock, unknown before 1924 in such northerly waters, are now caught in large numbers along the west coast of Greenland. Fish such as mackerel and tunny, once rarely seen around Iceland, have been taken regularly there since 1928. Other species, such as cod, have moved to spawning grounds on Iceland's north coast. The arctic port of Murmansk now provides more than two thirds of the entire Soviet fish catch. The world's biggest shrimp beds have lately been discovered 1,500 miles from the pole off western Greenland. The polar basin itself was long thought lacking in marine life, but Commander James Calvert reported with awe that as he piloted the *Skate* toward the pole, a school of fish "several miles long" streamed past his vessel's specially rigged "window" for undersea viewing.

In the coming development of the Arctic, its marine life should provide food for local settlers as well as for the world at large. But the future of the Arctic as a habitat for members of civilized societies depends finally upon the existence of renewable food resources on land. Civilized peoples have always depended upon a foundation of agriculture, and if man is really going to occupy the Arctic's political frontiers, develop its transport lines and exploit its natural resources, he will have to find and develop food supplies close at hand.

MINERAL PRODUCTION: NORTH AMERICAN ARCTIC

The table below lists latest figures for the annual production of important minerals in Alaska and arctic Canada (the Northwest Territories and the Yukon).

ALASKA

Copper:	82,000 lbs.
Gold:	168,197 troy oz.
Silver:	26,000 troy oz.
Mercury:	338,884 lbs.
Coal:	722,000 tons
Natural Gas:	246,000,000 cubic ft.
Crude Petroleum:	558,000 barrels
Sand and Gravel:	6,013,000 tons
Clay:	1,150 tons
Stone:	275,000 tons

ARCTIC CANADA

Copper:	1,250,000 lbs.
Gold:	489,262 troy oz.
Cadmium:	141,750 lbs.
Nickel:	4,700,000 lbs.
Lead:	21,592,456 lbs.
Silver:	6,975,700 troy oz.
Zinc:	13,246,532 lbs.
Uranium:	919,333 lbs.
Coal:	3,879 tons
Natural Gas:	67,189,000,000 cubic ft.
Crude Petroleum:	430,319 barrels

Here the Russians hold one advantage over Western Hemisphere countries: ice-age glaciers covered somewhat less of their extreme northern territories. There is more and better soil in many parts of Siberia than at comparable latitudes in Canada. North of the sixtieth parallel the Soviet Union has more than a million acres under cultivation; Canada has scarcely a thousand. Both the Canadians and the Russians have made considerable efforts to select new types of wheat and other grains that will mature in a shorter growing season, and the Russians have experimented boldly with schemes for treating seeds with radioactive stimulants before planting in the hope of getting them to germinate earlier.

All of this, however, has taken place south of the tree line, which happens to extend well to the north in Europe and Asia. In the far north, cultivation of crops has yet to be achieved. In the remote future it may be possible to build huge truck-garden greenhouses in these coldest regions, lighting and heating them by atomic power. It may also be possible some day by controlled evolution to breed plants or animals that can resist far-northern cold. But the likeliest arctic agriculture of the future will domesticate animals and plants that are already native to the region.

AT present the only domestic animal found in the Arctic is the reindeer. The peoples along the arctic coasts of Europe and Asia have herded reindeer for thousands of years. The Lapps of modern Norway have formed cooperatives to care for the animals, and to market the meat and skins. The Soviet Union, looking for new food sources, has given great attention to modernizing herds and standardizing management of its reindeer, which are numbered in millions.

The basic business of any animal husbandry is the conversion of grass into meat and hides. Vilhjalmur Stefansson, the arctic explorer-scientist, has said that the tundra could support 40 million head of reindeer and rival the Australian sheep country as one of the world's great meat-exporting areas. In such a development, the wide northern spaces of our own continent could play a significant part. So far the North American Arctic has been the range of the caribou, the wild brother of the reindeer. The domesticated reindeer was introduced to Alaska at the end of the 19th Century when Sheldon Jackson, an American missionary, imported 1,280 reindeer from Siberia to provide a dependable source of livelihood for Eskimos. The grazing lands of western Alaska proved ideal for reindeer, but the Eskimos are primarily hunters, and a hunting people usually do not make good herders. In the 1920s Nome businessmen took a hand in managing the enterprise, merging the flocks and marketing the reindeer meat in the United States. For a time the herds jumped 30 per cent in size from year to year, and were further swelled when wild caribou joined them. But the United States government decided to restrict reindeer-owning to so-called native people of Alaska. Today, with the exception of a government-owned herd on Nunivak Island in the Bering Sea, there are virtually no reindeer left in Alaska.

The Canadian government bought a herd from the Nome enterprisers, and in one of the most notable animal drives in history the 2,370 reindeer were herded 1,200 miles across the arctic tundra to the Mackenzie River delta. There a reindeer station was established. But the Eskimos of Canada proved as slow as those of Alaska in taking to animal husbandry. Finally in 1959 the

Canadian government changed its policy of leaving the reindeer to the Eskimos, and started a new program to make reindeer herding a factor in the economic development of northern Canada. Now the Canadian tundra may at last come into its own as a great grazing ground.

A second northern animal that may figure in an arctic agriculture of the future is the musk ox. It thrives on the tundra, requiring neither barns nor winter feed. Though capable of producing meat and hide, it is most valuable for the soft under-wool that sheathes its body like a mattress beneath its outer guard hairs. This under-wool, called quviut, is finer than cashmere and can be spun into delicate yarn for fine sweaters and other luxury clothing. It can be boiled without shrinking and will take any dye. In the commercial experiments to which it has been subjected it has been described as the world's finest natural wool.

The musk ox of course is a wild creature. But since 1954 experiments have been conducted in Vermont with a small pilot herd captured on the Canadian barrens, to determine whether the musk ox is suitable for domestication. A domestic animal is created by man through selective breeding, and domestication has no necessary connection with the animal's tameness. Some domestic animals in fact have been bred for their ferocity. Musk oxen have shown themselves to be readily adaptable to human management, and are intelligent and easily tamed. At first the animals must be selected mainly for their resistance to disease. Then attention may be given to those which grow fastest and produce the most quviut. After that it should be possible to establish a breeding farm in the Arctic where the herd can be expanded and problems of range management can be worked out. A market for quviut is assured: a number of large textile companies have shown an eagerness to purchase the wool.

IN the American north, fundamental research and experimenting are only getting started on the problems of creating the conditions for an enduring civilized life. The Russians got a head start in studying all these problems, and they work with much greater emphasis on long-range planning. Up to now, Soviet arctic research has been greater than that of all the other nations put together

Since 1937 the Russians have placed at least 10 scientific parties on polar floes for one to three years at a time, landed perhaps 30 teams a year for briefer observations at predetermined spots, and dropped automatic weather beacons all over the Arctic (some within 200 miles of the Canadian and Alaskan coasts) to transmit data on ice drift, air temperature and wind speed and direction. One team discovered the huge Lomonosov undersea mountain ridge that cuts across the polar sea floor from Siberia to Ellesmere Island. The sum of their scientific effort enables the Russians to forecast weather, plan military installations and budget their arctic resources with unrivaled efficiency and thoroughness. Reading scientific papers from the big Soviet All-Union Arctic Institute at Leningrad, the Canadians found that the Russians knew more about Canada's northernmost shores than they themselves did. The discovery was one reason why Canada launched its Polar Continental Shelf Project in 1959.

The Russians are particularly far ahead in their studies of the arctic ice. To speed their coastal convoys, they have set themselves the task of forecasting ice conditions eight to 10 months in advance. Finding that patches of pack ice clog summer navigation at certain points along the Siberian coast, they have tried spreading coal and sand on the ice to speed melting. The theory was that the sun's heat, most of which is reflected back into space by the ice, would be absorbed by a dark-colored layer on top of the ice, and so would melt it faster. The trick worked, clearing up a bad obstruction in 1959 in the Yenisey River estuary.

This led some Soviet engineers to talk about getting rid of all arctic ice this way. One said that if planes would dust the polar pack ice with crisscrossing strips of coal dust, the Arctic would become a sea of ice cubes; these would float off into the North Atlantic and leave the polar basin open to year-round shipping and to balmy winds. But Harry Wexler, chief of meteorological research for the United States Weather Bureau, scoffs at this idea. To lay a checkerboard of black .004 inch deep across the whole Arctic, he points out, would take one and a half billion tons of carbon black—and something like 150 million dust-dropping flights. Furthermore, just after the coal dust is dropped, it might snow.

Soviet Engineer P. M. Borisov has a still more ambitious plan for melting the ice and changing the weather. He proposes building a 46-mile dam across the Bering Strait, then pumping out the cold arctic water so that warmer water would flow in from the North Pacific. Others have suggested exploding hydrogen bombs to melt the arctic ice. But such fancy schemes could defeat their very purpose. Scientists at the Lamont Geological Observatory contend that the ice ages of the past came upon the world precisely when the Arctic happened to be *free* of ice. Winds blowing across the open polar sea, they say, picked up moisture and dumped it in snow that kept piling up until thick ice sheets covered the land southward as far as southern Illinois. If this theory is right, then the melting of arctic ice, far from mellowing the climate of Canada, Alaska and Siberia, would bury tremendous areas of these lands under glaciers.

THE habitable Arctic of the future, then, is not likely to be shaped by such grandiose schemes. Humanity does not have enough basic knowledge to try modifying weather on a large scale. The main thing is to widen and intensify the research in the north. It is also essential, as Vilhjalmur Stefansson has said, to accept the Arctic as it is, and see it as a challenge: man has to conquer the north, and force it to be useful to him. The Russians understand this very well, and have seen that the vast resources and geographic location of their own northern territory can make a significant contribution to national wealth and strength. They have deliberately pushed development along their northern fringes until Siberia has become the fastest-growing part of the Russian empire.

Today it is Soviet Siberia that is being opened up. Tomorrow it will be the turn of the American Arctic, whose potential for a contribution to man's future may well be even bigger. Its riches in resources and potential food supplies, its strategic and military importance, are already known in general outline. Its Eskimos and Indians can teach others much about living there, and the soldiers and scientists are daily finding out more. Though we need not look for another Klondike rush, we know that the north has things the world needs. It takes no special foresight to see that as man continues his progress from the tropics toward the poles, the coming arctic boom is only decades away.

TWO CREWMEN WATCH AS THE U.S. NUCLEAR SUBMARINE "SKATE" RISES THROUGH THE POLAR ICE PACK IN ONE OF 10 SUCH THRUSTS

"Great Tomorrow Land"

There are great riches in the Arctic—and equally great problems of climate and transportation standing in the way of their development. But military necessity has brought in people and planes, nuclear submarines and road builders, all crowding the region as never before. The invasion is opening the way for a flood tide of pioneers in "the great tomorrow land."

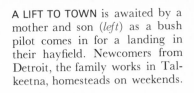

A LIFT TO TOWN is awaited by a mother and son (*left*) as a bush pilot comes in for a landing in their hayfield. Newcomers from Detroit, the family works in Talkeetna, homesteads on weekends.

A RACE WITH WINTER drives pioneers (*below*) to build a log barn for one of them to live in with his horses. While the men put up the barn, their wives helped out by canning moose and bear meat.

Hard Life on a New Frontier

Housing and jobs are scarce, prices are sky-high, darkness and cold rule much of the year—but still the pioneers come to seek a new life in the frontier state of Alaska. Population jumped 75 per cent in the 1950s, and though the biggest contingent is there under orders—66,000 servicemen and their dependents—some 2,000 letters a month come to the state from prospective voluntary settlers. Among these were 37 Detroiters who, led by a dance-studio manager and calling themselves "fifty-niners," trekked 4,500 miles by road in 1959. Here are pictures of what faced 13 of them who dug in 100 miles north of Anchorage.

IN A QUONSET HUT brought from Anchorage, the homesteaders forget their hardships for a while and recall early pioneers as one cavorts in a Gold Rush dance-hall costume.

BY DAWN'S LATE LIGHT at 8:30 a.m., a school bus stops for children waiting outside Anchorage. Buses must come within one and a half miles of each child's home—which can still mean stiff twice-a-day hikes in winter cold and darkness. There are compensations, such as frolics in the snow at recess in schoolyards lit by the glow from classroom windows.

Daily Life in the Darkness

LONG JOHNS hang on a line at Anchorage, where they will get board-stiff but fairly dry. Even a trip to hang the wash can help ward off "cabin fever," especially for young mothers.

In Fairbanks, northernmost city of Alaska, midwinter temperatures average around 12° below zero, and the horizon-hugging sun shines only four or five hours a day. Winters in Anchorage, 280 miles to the south, are not much milder or brighter. Housebound people develop the wild yearning for sun and space called "cabin fever." Still, most of them go cheerfully about their afternoon business by flashlight, or go skiing under floodlights. But in summer one can play golf at midnight. Such subarctic novelties—along with magnificent scenery, informal living, chances of fortune and the pioneer's satisfying sense of purposeful adventure—make most settlers from the states to the south say that they would never go back.

THE WAN WINTER SUN, shown in multiple exposure passing over Fairbanks, rises only about 2° above the horizon. This view is south over the residential district toward the distant Alaska Range. Fairbanks, 115 miles south of the Arctic Circle, is Alaska's second largest city (population 13,311) and the terminus of the Alaska Railroad and Alaska Highway.

A MUSK-OX HERD FLEES A LOW-FLYING PLANE SCOUTING FOR CALVES TO TAME. THE CALF AT LEFT BELOW CAME FROM THIS HERD

A CAPTURED CALF, herded by seaplane, seized while swimming and flown to a Canadian base camp, is carried struggling to the shore by John Teal (*right*) and a young helper.

The Taming of the Musk Ox

One of the Arctic's most interesting potential resources is the shaggy tundra animal called the musk ox—which has no musk glands and is not an ox. The creature looks like a cross between cattle and bison, bears a scientific name (ovibos) that means sheep-ox, has a tender meat that tastes something like both beef and mutton, and is related to the goat and antelope family.

Once hunted almost to extinction, musk oxen became a far less important source of food to arctic dwellers than caribou, seals, walruses and fish. But the musk ox bears a prime commercial asset: under its long, coarse outer hair is a thick undercoat of wool that surpasses cashmere in soft lightness and strength. A cashmere goat yields only three ounces of wool per year; a musk ox produces six pounds of its fine fiber—and domestic breeding could increase this yield. Encouraged by explorer Vilhjalmur Stefansson, an anthropologist and arctic specialist named John J. Teal Jr. captured some musk-ox calves in Canada several years ago and has been experimenting in domesticating them on his Vermont farm.

A PLACID OX, far from its home in Canada's Northwest Territories, plods through a Vermont farm pond. The animals are easily tamed, playful and intelligent. But the summer heat of New England has proved fatal to newborn musk-ox calves, and Teal's domestication project may be transferred to a farther-north farm of the University of Alaska.

MEN OF THE WORLD'S "TOP" FIGHTER SQUADRON HEAD FOR QUARTERS FROM THEIR INTERCEPTOR PLANES ON THULE'S ICE RUNWAYS

ON THE "DEW" LINE a radar station sweeps the sky for enemy bombers from a peak in the Canadian Arctic. More than 50 stations form a 4,500-mile radar fence across the Arctic.

Cold Bastions of Cold War

On these pages are shown some of the defense installations which have drawn history's greatest migration to the Arctic. Some 20,000 workers—almost equal to the population of Canada's vast Northwest Territories—were employed in building the Distant Early Warning (DEW) Line. Its stations, manned by 1,300 persons, now stretch from Iceland to the Aleutians. The more powerful Ballistic Missile Early Warning System outpost at Thule, Greenland (*opposite*), cost $500 million and took two years to build. A similar installation has been completed at Clear, Alaska, and a third will scan the northern and eastern skies from Fylingdales Moor, England.

Only 13 military men and 900 civilian technicians operate the Thule station, but the entire complex there, including a major air base, requires a community of 6,000 Americans living less than a thousand miles from the North Pole.

THE POLAR DEFENSE LINE begins at Thule, Greenland, where radar antennae loom in the arctic night. Four antennae, each 400 feet wide and 165 feet high, with a 3,500- mile range, keep watch on Soviet skies. Aided by computers, they can give North American defense headquarters 15 minutes' warning of a missile's probable point of impact.

8

The Great Antarctic Laboratory

IN terms of exploitability, the farthest north and the uttermost south are worlds apart. The future of the Arctic, which is crammed with resources and fairly accessible, is not merely unquestionable but undeniable; it lies no further ahead than the next generation and its nature, for better or worse, will be one prolonged boom. Antarctica, on the other hand, is not about to become either a crossroads of supersonic travel or an industrial miracle; it is a fascinating laboratory and, as far ahead as anyone can see, is unlikely to be anything more than that. It is still locked in the grip of an ice age, the most isolated place on earth and the coldest as well. To this day no more than 1,000 people have lived through a winter there, and on the whole continent there is not a single permanent human inhabitant.

Yet there is no point in underestimating the Antarctic simply because its practical utilization is remote. Looking far ahead, Admiral Richard E. Byrd, America's foremost authority on the south polar region, said shortly before his death in 1957: "In the immediate future there is nothing—we know that—but 100 years is a short time in the life of a nation, and we should think more of the future than we do." With an eye to that future seven nations have pushed claims to generous slices of antarctic territory. The United States, without making any territorial claims, has concentrated on acquiring knowledge of this cold new world. In 1961 the United States and 11 other countries including the Soviet Union ratified a treaty setting Antarctica aside as a preserve for scientific research. "It is in the interest of all mankind," the treaty says, "that Antarctica shall continue forever to be used exclusively for peaceful purposes and shall not become the scene or object of international discord." A major aim of the International Geophysical Year was the increase of knowledge about the Antarctic. Thus far the United States, Russia, Britain, Japan, Australia, Belgium, New Zealand, Norway, Argentina, Chile, France and South Africa have maintained bases there, and all lend advice, equipment and assistance to each other whenever it is needed. The United States and Russia even exchange scientists to work at each other's bases.

In 1961-1962, 174 American scientists and some 100 from other nations were "on the ice," as the antarctic men say, gathering the research data that must for a long time be the continent's most useful export. They have found it easier to discover new mysteries than to find answers for them. Some of Antarctica's biggest mountains, for instance, are thought to be an extension of the Chilean Andes, which raises the possibility that they could be as rich as the South American range in gold, tin and copper. In land where no other men have ever set foot, University of Minnesota geologists are now collecting rock specimens and mapping terrain of the Sentinel Range of the Ellsworth Mountains, perhaps the biggest unexplored range on earth. Today men look to the far north for iron to replace Minnesota's all but exhausted Mesabi Range; in a distant tomorrow the prospectors may turn to the far south. There are immense deposits of low-grade coal in Antarctica. The Russians have found small amounts of mica, graphite and iron. And the Australians think their "section" of the continent may contain uranium, lead and zinc.

The scientists are also taking seismic soundings of the antarctic ice to clear up a major mystery: will the continent's ice sheet grow or shrink if, as many of them expect, the earth's climate keeps on getting warmer? In other parts of the world, glaciers have been melting; the level of the oceans has risen by about two and a half inches in this century. But IGY researchers discovered that far more of the world's ice than was thought— more than 90 per cent—is locked up in the antarctic icecap. They learned that the ice sheet, so vast that the continent has sunk 1,600 to 3,300 feet into the earth's plastic mantle under its weight, is just about the size of the Laurentian glacier that spread across the eastern United States and Canada 14,000 to 18,000 years ago. This in itself is of interest to the scientists, for it means that a good deal can be learned in Antarctica now about North America's own glacial past. But what the scientists really want to know is whether the antarctic icecap is expanding or contracting. After some Homeric calculations, Pyotr Shumsky, the Russian IGY chief, announced in 1960 that the volume of ice in the Antarctic is growing at the rate of about 293 cubic miles a year. Annual snowfall, he figured, is about 612 cubic miles a year, but much of this is blown out to sea in the fierce antarctic storms. All together, in glaciologist Shumsky's computations, losses by blowing, evaporating, melting and the breaking away of icebergs

FOR PEACEFUL USES OF THE ANTARCTIC

An international agreement pledging the use of Antarctica for nonmilitary, scientific ends was signed in 1959 by representatives of 12 governments: Argentina, Australia, Belgium, Chile, the French Republic, Japan, New Zealand, Norway, the Union of South Africa, the U.S.S.R., the United Kingdom and the U.S. Some of its provisions are:

• "Antarctica shall be used for peaceful purposes only. There shall be prohibited . . . any measures of a military nature. . . ."

• "Freedom of scientific investigation in Antarctica and cooperation toward that end . . . shall continue. . . ."

• "Information regarding plans for scientific programs shall be exchanged to permit maximum economy and efficiency of operations: scientific personnel shall be exchanged in Antarctica between expeditions and stations; scientific observations and results from Antarctica shall be exchanged and made freely available."

• "Any nuclear explosions in Antarctica and the disposal there of radioactive waste material shall be prohibited. . . ."

add up to a little over 300 cubic miles, leaving a yearly surplus on the surface of about 300 cubic miles. Fritz Loewe of the French IGY party agrees that the inland ice appears to be growing. He suggests that it might be precisely the result of warmer temperatures in the world at large, which would lead in turn to heavier antarctic snowfall. Despite all this it is not known for sure whether the Antarctic's ice budget is in balance or not. But if all its ice should melt—and a world-wide average temperature increase of only a few degrees might be enough to do the trick—the level of the oceans could rise over 200 feet. This would be enough to submerge half the world's populated area and most of its great cities, including New York, London, Paris and Tokyo. Such invasions by the sea have happened before, and could happen again. If something like this should be in store for the world in coming centuries, the polar regions are where we will find it out.

A more urgent line of inquiry is the investigation of Antarctica's coastal waters. Someday these icy depths, rich in mineral nutrients, could become an important auxiliary source of human food. They also swarm with the microscopic plants and animals which are basic food for red krill, the shrimplike animal that the antarctic whales eat. Engineers have proposed building ships that could push giant sieves through the water, harvesting these planktonic foods in the same way whales do. Even if this could be done, ways would have to be devised to make the plankton palatable. On the 1951 French expedition to the antarctic coast, a gifted chef found ways to turn the emperor penguin and the South Polar skua into *Rôti d'Empereur* and *Suprème de Skua sur Canapé;* but a dish of Euphausia (or krill), the tiny creature relished by whales, proved beyond even Gallic culinary skill. Though the expedition leader found the dish, served with sauce *Américaine,* "absolutely succulent," that night Euphausia took revenge and for two days the whole party took to their cots.

There is another way in which the Antarctic might augment man's food supply. "It would be entirely feasible," Admiral Byrd once told Congress, "to employ the Antarctic as a vast freezer where we could store the enormous food surpluses we now have in this country." The Reverend Daniel Linehan, head of Boston College's Geophysics Department, believes that the world could cope with the population boom by cultivating all land available and storing the surplus food in the Antarctic. On a 1955 expedition with the Navy, Father Linehan ate bread left behind by the Shackleton party 50 years ago. "It was a little dry," he reported, "but otherwise it tasted fine." There is not much risk of spoilage: at Little America geographer Paul Siple could find only one bacterium per pint of snow.

Because the United States has made such a big effort in Antarctica, it is ahead in the friendly race to explore the continent's possibilities. In the space age, when the Antarctic is likely to take on greater strategic and scientific importance, this effort may start to pay off. The United States has placed one of its stations right at the South Pole. So far, the 11 scientists at the station have been measuring temperature, snowfall, ice thickness, solar radiation and earth magnetism, and making other geophysical studies. However, from this vantage point it would also be possible to survey all the southern heavens. Because of its location on the spin axis of the earth, a single tracking station at the South Pole could keep continuous watch on any space-probe launching south of the equator. A tracking station at this

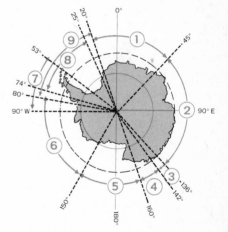

ANTARCTIC CLAIMS are mapped above. They include sectors staked out by Norway (1), Australia (2 and 4), France (3), New Zealand (5), Chile (7), Argentina (8) and Great Britain (9). The U.S. (6) has neither made claims nor recognized those of other nations. Despite some territorial disputes, scientific parties have always moved freely in the Antarctic.

point also could take advantage of the fact that the best satellite orbit, the only one that covers all parts of the globe, is a north-south track over both poles. Such a station could collect information from every pass of a polar-orbiting satellite. Finally, the Antarctic may be the best spot for launching manned trips into outer space. This is because the Van Allen radiation belt, which envelops the earth, is thinnest at the two geomagnetic poles. Presumably astronauts leaving or returning to earth via Antarctica would be in the least danger from this zone of intense radiation.

The United States has installed a 1,500-kilowatt nuclear reactor at its air terminal at McMurdo Sound, and others will eventually go to the South Pole and Byrd Stations. The reactors will pay for themselves through savings on fuel (which costs perhaps 50 times as much as in the United States when shipped into Antarctica). But their real importance may be in providing the electric power needed to turn the South Pole base into a major polar tracking station and a crossroads of space science.

The reactors can also provide power for radar and other equipment needed to open up the continent for flying through the long, black antarctic winter. Against the day when airliners span both poles, Rear Admiral David M. Tyree, Navy commander in the Antarctic, wants to see a jet airfield hewn out of the mainland near McMurdo Sound, at Marble Point in Taylor Dry Valley. Says Tyree: "I visualize some day a community might exist in Taylor Dry Valley. Perhaps there could be a tourist hotel, and many would want to travel the scenic air route up the famous Beardmore Glacier over which Scott toiled on his march to the Pole."

In the process of probing and taming the continent, men are gaining more knowledge about man himself. The white antarctic desert turns out to be a unique laboratory for the study of the human biological and psychological systems under conditions of extreme cold and isolation. Though modern machines and techniques now enable men virtually to take their preferred climate with them even to the pole, the story of life on the bleak inner plateau still remains a narrative of survival. The margin between comfort and disaster is always very slim, and for all but about five months of the year the men at these bases are utterly on their own with no possibility of aid from outside.

A CITY UNDER GLASS could make antarctic colonization feasible. Nuclear generators outside the dome would provide power and regulate the temperature inside. A light on the tower at center would act as an artificial sun in the dark months.

COLD is the main adversary. But man is a highly adaptable animal. His body has built-in thermostatic controls that can do certain things to offset cold: it can generate more body heat by exercise; and it can conserve that heat by contracting the blood vessels near the skin. If the skin's temperature falls far enough, the thermostat causes shivering to set in, an involuntary form of muscular exercise that may temporarily increase body heat. "It's shivering," says a physiologist, "which largely explains why so many are cold but so few are frozen." Such internal control enabled naked Indians living in the near-freezing temperatures of Tierra del Fuego, 600 miles north of the Antarctic, to survive for generations.

Not that shivering would keep anybody from freezing to death in the antarctic climate. To survive polar cold, man must manipulate his environment. He can do this in three ways—by adding or taking off clothing and by taking shelter, both of which regulate heat, and by eating a diet which increases his heat production. In the Arctic the Eskimos, by living on a high-protein diet of caribou and seal meat, have made the third way work notably well. But inland on the antarctic continent, animal life is rare, and man must bring his own food from outside. The early explorers brought pemmican, a brownish, greasy-looking mixture of fat and meat extract so rich that in temperate climates it turns people's stomachs. "There seems to be something in the cold climate," wrote Frank Debenham of the Scott expedition, "which leads to a desire for fats and the ability to digest it." On one five-week sledging expedition three members of the Scott party tried a rough and ready experiment. One ate half pemmican (protein and fat) and half biscuit (carbohydrate), one ate mainly pemmican, and the third ate mainly biscuit. After the second week, the first two were thriving but the third, on the biscuit diet, was suffering repeated frostbite. The test led Scott to order balanced pemmican-biscuit rations for his pole dash. When the supply ran out it was starvation, not cold, that took the lives of Scott and his party just 11 miles from a one-ton food cache.

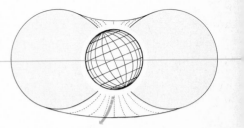

THE VAN ALLEN BELT of dangerous radiation (indicated in blue) has funnel-shaped gaps at the magnetic poles, where rockets with human passengers could be launched with relative safety. The arrow traces a South Magnetic Pole take-off.

Aʟʟ told, over 135 deaths have been recorded in Antarctica since Captain James Cook first circumnavigated its icy seas a century and a half ago, and the merciless cold was at least a contributing factor in many of them. One snow-borne hazard of cold that has taken a number of lives is "white-out." This is an eerie phenomenon caused by daylight penetrating an overcast sky and reflecting back and forth between snow and sky until the horizon disappears and nothing but white meets the eye. In the Antarctic's bewildering white-outs, skiers fall down, drivers topple off their tractors and pilots fly their planes right into the ground. At Ellsworth Base in 1958 a helicopter pilot lost his bearings in a sudden white-out and crashed to his death, and a rescue pilot narrowly escaped when the helicopter he thought he was flying level bumped at a steep angle against the ground. It has now become almost standard helicoptering practice to throw out some dark object on a line to help the pilot tell whether he is flying 20 feet above the ground surface —or one foot.

Snow blindness is another menace of the cold country. It is a form of temporary blindness caused by burning of the conjunctiva of the eye by snow-reflected ultraviolet rays of a certain wave length. Traveling on the Greenland icecap without his protective dark glasses one dazzling spring day, the explorer Dr. Kaare Rodahl, an expert on low-temperature physiology, found the landscape going first pink and then red before his eyes. Soon "my eyes felt as if someone had thrown a handful of sand into them." Disabled and in intense pain, Rodahl was forced to halt, improvise a snow shelter, crawl in and wait three days for his sight to come back.

Frostbite, the actual freezing of tissues, is a common antarctic calamity. When Admiral George Dufek's party made the first landing at the pole in a twin-engine Douglas transport plane in 1956, they had hardly planted the American flag and taken pictures in the 58°-below-zero cold when they saw patches of skin turning yellow-gray on each other's cheeks. The old explorers, hauling their sledges into the flaying winds, used to watch one another's faces for these telltale patches and for blisters, which signify a more serious stage of frostbite.

The danger increases if a man gets wet, because water drains heat from the skin even faster than air. The old explorers tried hard to keep their sleeping bags dry, free from perspiration and from outdoor moisture, and they constantly had to fight frostbite in their extremities. "In the sleeping bag at night," wrote Edward Wilson of the Scott expedition, "everything on you thaws. You feel wet through all night, not merely damp but sopping." Nowadays it is not that bad, for equipment is at hand to dry things out in the night, but plenty of toes and fingers still get frost-nipped. Expedition doctors treat frostbite by thawing with a mild form of heat— never by rubbing with snow, which would only draw out body heat and might even break the skin.

Suitably clothed, man can endure terrific extremes of cold. Even on the day in August 1958 that the thermometer at the Soviet high-plateau base of Vostok registered a near-record cold of 125.3° below, men were not kept indoors. The camp commandant simply required that they bundle up, and ordered them not to go out alone. When temperatures dropped below -112°, he allowed his meteorologists to go outdoors for 15 minutes at a time; when the thermometer showed -121° or lower he limited outdoor trips to 10 minutes. Swathed in furs, the men carried 40-watt, pocket-size batteries and electric heaters that warmed their hands, feet and chests. They wore face masks fitted with corrugated hose to draw warm air from inside their clothing.

Actually the limit for efficient outdoor work under exposed conditions is reached at temperatures far less severe than these. According to Dr. Rodahl the limit is in the neighborhood of 40° below. Beyond that point, "every minor detail of routine becomes a major operation requiring utmost caution." When the roof blew off the meteorology hut at Vostok it took the men three weeks, working with flashlights in the dark at -104°, to make repairs. When Scott and his men were on their last march to the pole, pitching and striking camp took them up to nine hours. A man dressed to walk a long way in temperatures much below -40° is so hampered by his bulky clothing that he is soon likely to use up his strength.

Proper cold-weather clothing is still an antarctic headache. The Navy's latest antarctic manual specifies all kinds of fancy garments for its men— waffle-weave, heat-trapping underwear, nylon-insulated parkas and pants, helmets, masks, heated boots—and then apologizes: "A program for improvement of this clothing will continue." Sir Vivian Fuchs says that members of his Trans-Antarctic Expedition of 1957-1958 spent much time "modifying" their clothes, and notes wryly that the changes only seemed to make their outfits look more like those pictured in books on Scott's and Shackleton's expeditions. "Nothing we have devised," says an American Army polar specialist, "has been able to equal the loosely tailored fur garments of the Eskimo." When an Eskimo chases his quarry on a hunt, the chill air flows into and out of his flapping caribou-skin parka to prevent overheating. Later, when he rests, his clothing settles around him and provides an insulating efficiency that is hard to surpass.

Of man's three basic ways of making the antarctic environment livable, by far the most effective has been his use of shelter. But he has had to bring his shelter with him: in Antarctica the prefab has really come into its own. Even in 1910 the early explorers' huts were prefabricated, but there is a great contrast between such huts and the camps of today and the air-conditioned communities planned for tomorrow. At McMurdo Sound, close by Scott's old base hut, there is a village of 168 (1,000 when the "summer people" arrive in November), with a post office, laundry,

PX, tank farm and disbursing office all facing a thoroughfare called Main Street. The entire South Pole station was prefabricated in the United States and hauled to the site by Globemasters flying 850 miles in from the coastal ice strip at McMurdo Sound. Within four weeks the laboratories, instruments and power plants were assembled and 18 men were at home and at work in a community of six huts linked by scaffolded passages beneath the snow. Airdrops of the 760 tons of gear went on for nine more weeks. High-powered fans are used to keep an even heat within the huts; otherwise the temperature would be 50° colder on the floor than at the ceiling and men in lower bunks would need extra blankets. But at least, on the all-but-germfree Antarctic, nobody catches cold.

On the trail, the contrasts of living are still greater. Early explorers had to pitch tents or build snow-cover at their rest stops. In such conditions, wrote Alex Cherry-Garrard in *The Worst Journey in the World*, even lighting the candle in the morning was "a heroic business. Moisture from our breath collected on our matches. Sometimes it was necessary to try four or five boxes before a match struck." Then the stove had to be lit. Even with the help of a "marvelous" set of pans invented by the Norwegian explorer Fridtjof Nansen and "guaranteed" to use over 90 per cent of the heat of the precious paraffin fuel, cooking on a cold spring journey could be a tricky, time-consuming maneuver.

Life on the trail was brutal when Scott, Shackleton and Amundsen fought their way across the icecap. Today scientists ride in motorized shelters. Stopping each night on their summer "traverse" runs across the ice sheet, they eat and then spread their sleeping bags high and dry, in the snug, heated cabins of their broad-tracked, 10-ton Snocat tractors.

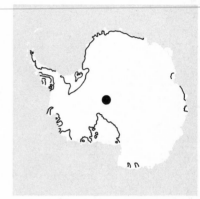

ANTARCTICA TODAY is covered almost completely by a thick icecap which leaves only a few edges of the shore exposed. In some places this glaciation extends beyond the coast line to form giant floating ice shelves. The dot is the South Pole.

UNTIL their shelters became so elaborate, the hazards men faced in high latitudes were overwhelmingly of the physical kind. Early polar explorers complained of such ailments as "igloo back." For Nansen, spending the winter of 1855-1856 in virtual hibernation in a low stone hut on Franz Josef Land, rheumatism was the big trouble. When Admiral Byrd wintered alone in the interior in 1934, he lost 75 pounds and nearly lost his life by slow monoxide poisoning from a leaky stove. And for the first men who set up camps on the high antarctic plateau in 1957, the ordeal was grimly physical. The five pioneers at the Russian Sovietskaya base, 12,280 feet above sea level, suffered headaches, shortness of breath, pounding of the heart and low blood pressure. At night they woke with the feeling that they were choking. Though camp physician V. Konstantinov cooked extra rations, the men lost weight alarmingly the first month. That was also the experience at the American South Pole Station 800 miles away, where seven of the 18 men lost more than 25 pounds in the first three months. Then they became acclimated and at both camps, in the comparative idleness of winter, their weight leveled off.

In antarctic camps today, the stress under which men live is more psychological than physiological; it comes mainly from the sense of isolation. Confined up to a year in close quarters, they may develop signs of "cabin fever." Some lose appetite and weight, though most tend to compensate for boredom and frustration by eating much more. As the six-month-long night of winter settles over the camp, spirits fall. The normal rhythms of daylight and dark lose their meaning. Many suffer from "The

ANTARCTICA OF THE FUTURE may be ice-free if the earth warms up. The melt-water would raise the level of the oceans but the land also would rise when rid of its great ice burden. The resulting shape of the continent is shown above.

Big Eye," abandoning their cots to sit sleepless till "morning" among the old magazines and phonograph records of the mess hut. Others develop "The Long Eye." In the words of a sailor: "They stare right at you, but never see you. They never say a word to anybody. They have a 12-foot stare in a 10-foot room."

In such times, a man is glad for his work. Some haul in snow for the camp water supply. Some go out to look after the sled dogs in their snow tunnels. Others raise bunkside tomatoes. In his year as scientific leader at Wilkes Station, biologist Carl Eklund read 57 books. According to Gordon Cartwright, first American scientist to winter-over with the Soviets, the Russians play checkers. An important part of life at American stations is the chance to talk on the short-wave radio to ham operators back home, many of whom are willing to arrange "phone patches"—that is, place collect long-distance telephone calls for a man. A device placed in the ham operator's telephone enables the man at the pole to talk directly with home. Liquor under proper control is regarded in the Antarctic as a useful aid in reducing tension, and about once a week most camps hold what the Australians call a "ding." Movies are popular. For some reason one camp took a particular liking to the 1940 film, *Pride and Prejudice.* It was shown over and over. When for a change it was shown with the sound turned off, the men chanted in unison the dialogue which they knew by heart.

SOME day, when nuclear reactors are installed at every inland station and planes can fly in and out of the continent in all seasons and in all but the fiercest blizzards, this kind of isolation will end. Then men—and women—may live in Antarctica under conditions a little more like those prevailing in the rest of the world. Some engineers have proposed big "shelter domes" of glass that would seal off whole camps in their own greenhouse climate. More likely, if man is ever to gain an enduring foothold in the ice, he will have to make better use of the environment and live within the ice itself.

This is not so farfetched as it may sound. At Camp Century, 800 miles from the North Pole on the Greenland icecap, the United States Army is cutting out over a mile of tunnels for an under-ice community to house 100 men. Snow-removing machinery long used in the Swiss Alps to keep railroad tracks clear in winter is doing the job. Open trenches are cut, steel arches are placed over them and snow is blown over the arches. After the snow hardens, the arches are pulled out and moved on to shape another tunnel roof. In Camp Century's corridors temperatures will be regulated to about 15° above zero to keep down melting. In the living quarters temperatures will be maintained in the comfortable 60s. The one problem yet to be solved at Camp Century is how to cope with the plastic flow that occurs in ice, a force that is capable of twisting steel girders like taffy. But the flow, though irresistible, is very slow; the Army engineers think they can overcome it by shaving and reshaving Camp Century's inner walls as the ice slowly closes in. If the experts can solve the problem of plastic flow, whole communities of several thousand may eventually be established under the ice of both the Arctic and the Antarctic. Then at last it may become possible to call man the inhabitant of all the continents—including the coldest one.

A SNOW SQUALL SHROUDS THE U.S. BASE AT McMURDO SOUND. THE SEA HERE IS USUALLY FROZEN AND FORMS A LANDING STRIP

The Big Push South

Ten thousand men of a dozen nations visited Antarctica during the recent International Geophysical Year, twice as many as had set foot on the continent in all the 138 years since its discovery. Under this massive assault by science, many of the continent's mysteries began to give way. The IGY is over, but the arduous work of opening Antarctica goes on, now warmed and lighted by atomic fuels.

A 10-TON TANK of steel is gently lowered onto a cargo sled at the edge of the ice as a Navy transport unloads part of a nuclear power plant for installation at McMurdo Sound.

A TRACTOR FLEET, dragging heavy sleds loaded with the reactor components (*below*), crawls across the ice toward the McMurdo base, six miles from the ship's anchorage.

NUCLEA
PLANT
MCMURI
FREEZE
PKG.

NO
STEP

Nuclear Power for Antarctica

The Navy transport U.S.S. *Arneb* was made fast to the edge of the ice at McMurdo Sound on December 14, 1961. From her holds the crewmen unloaded the components of a 1,500-kilowatt nuclear power plant, the first of four the United States will install in Antarctica. The reactor can generate five times the electricity McMurdo previously had available. The annual operating cost is estimated at $750,000, compared with $1,200,-000 to operate conventional diesel generators producing an equivalent amount of power.

The advantages are even more striking at less accessible sites. All supplies for the U.S. South Pole Station must be airlifted 850 miles from McMurdo Sound. The station burns 190 gallons of oil a day for heat and electricity, which costs $685 to deliver at the pole. A 1,000-kilowatt nuclear power plant small enough to be delivered by air is being designed for installation at Byrd Station in 1965. A similar unit is planned for the base at the South Pole and another unit will be added to the plant at McMurdo. Despite its high initial cost (close to six million dollars for McMurdo's installation), atomic power is a practical answer to the problems of providing heat and electricity for operations in Antarctica. It may provide the key to opening the continent to much more varied kinds of human activity.

MASSIVE UNITS AWAIT ASSEMBLY UNDER THE GREEN REACTOR BUILDING (BACKGROUND) ON A HILLSIDE SOUTHEAST OF THE BASE

SAMPLING SNOW, experts take cores from a pit dug in the ice near the South Pole. Snow melts slowly in the Antarctic and layers in the cores reveal centuries of snowfall.

SLICING A CORE, a glaciologist prepares samples for study. Air, pollen and dust trapped in snow that fell on Antarctica long ago can shed new light on the earth's history.

MEASURING MAGNETISM, a scientist (*left*) uses an instrument so sensitive it is kept in a room under the ice. A red light prevents film used in the experiments from fogging.

A BELOW-ZERO SHOWER outdoors at -6° F. can last only seconds but it is possible on a sunny, calm antarctic day. Water for this and all other purposes is melted from snow.

The Trial of the Cold

Man being essentially a tropical creature, no climate on earth is more inhospitable or potentially dangerous to him than that of Antarctica. Often required to work on floating sea ice, every visitor to the south polar region must accept the constant risk of being dumped in 28° brine where immersion can bring death within 15 minutes. Once safe on land (or icecap) men must stoke their bodies with large quantities of food to maintain body warmth. An average of 5,000 calories a day is needed by a man working in the Antarctic, compared to the 3,500 he would require in a temperate climate. Yet, given proper nutrition and clothing, the human being is remarkably adaptable to the cold. At a Soviet antarctic station, for example, scientists have worked out of doors when the thermometer has dipped to the record low temperature on earth—126.9° below zero.

AN ICY PLUNGE tests Navy submersion suits (*below*) which are worn by swimmers to rescue persons who fall into the water. The bright orange color assures maximum visibility.

A CHILLED GEOLOGIST returns to base from a collecting trip as mist cuts visibility. A beard keeps his face warm, but collects frost condensed from his breath by the cold air.

The Demands of a Precarious Life Far from Home

Men volunteer for polar duty for much the same reasons that will draw them some day to the planets: to seek fame in the dangerous job of exploring the unknown, to escape the problems of life back home or, in the case of the scientist, to pursue a field of study wherever it may lead. Whatever his motive, the success and happiness of the antarctic visitor is ultimately determined by factors beyond his control. Age is vital: men between 25 and 45 perform best. Younger men lack stability; older men lack vigor. Near-perfect health is required, for medical facilities are limited. Perhaps most important are a man's own inner resources: a sense of humor to shrug off privation, a flexibility that can adjust to unexpected dangers, a strength of character that can find contentment in loneliness or even in the care of a few gangling seedlings from home (*below*).

A SPINDLY VEGETABLE GARDEN SEEKS THE SUN IN THE PLASTIC BUBBLE WINDOW OF A BUILDING AT WILKES STATION, ANTARCTICA

CURLED IN A CRATE with his instruments on top, a scientist snatches a few moments of sleep and privacy at a temporary camp. With little to distinguish night from day, men may go for days without rest, sleeping only when exhausted. In the confined world of winter quarters, they alternate between a thirst for companionship and a desire to be alone.

185

II	Require Medical Supplies
≡	Require Doctor
F	Require Food and Water
⫫	Require Clothing
L	Require Fuel and Oil
◇	Require Map and Compass
V	Require Arms and Ammunition
W	Require Engineer
-	Require Signal Lamp
L	Aircraft Badly Damaged
X	Unable to Proceed
▷	Will Attempt Take-off
→	We Proceed This Direction
K	Show Direction to Proceed
✳	Don't Land Here
⬳	Land Here, Pointing Direction
Y	Yes, Affirmative
N	No, Negative
⌐⌐	Not Understood
LL	All Well

GROUND-TO-AIR CODE can be used by stranded people to communicate with airplanes. Signals, trampled in the snow or made of branches, cloth or stones, should be 8 to 10 feet long for easy spotting. They must contrast with the background.

Polar Do's and Don't's

The polar regions are not tolerant of mistakes. To prepare personnel for service in the Arctic or Antarctic, the U.S. Navy has prepared a 124-page book called the *Polar Manual*. Pungently written by Captain E. E. Hedblom, staff surgeon to the Navy's forces in the Antarctic during 1955-1959, the *Manual* ends with a terse list of Polar Do's and Don't's, a sobering summary of what can befall the careless visitor in the far north or south.

1. Dares are neither offered nor taken. Necessary risks are bad enough.

2. When leaving camp or ship, regardless of means of transportation, be sure you are adequately dressed, properly equipped, have a sleeping bag and sufficient rations to last out in the open 3 to 10 days. If flying, make sure *your* survival gear is aboard the plane. You may be stranded or have to walk home.

3. *Never* leave camp alone—at least *two* men per party on sea ice or hiking on land. The buddy system not only helps in prevention and early treatment of frostbite, but if you fall into the water, your buddy's efforts will probably save you. If you break a leg you have assistance and someone who knows where you are to go for help.

4. On shelf ice or glacier ice, parties *must* consist of *three* or more men, and they must rope together if in questionable crevasse country. In crevasse country trail breakers on skis must CONTINUALLY probe for crevasses with ice axes. In probing for tractor trail, longer, heavier probes (crowbars) must be used. Select camps on glacial ice with great care, and don't unrope except on thoroughly tested and *marked* areas.

5. If you feel cold, remember that exercise produces heat. A particularly good exercise is to tense both the extensors and flexors of the arms and legs at the same time. This produces heat without motion. However, don't overdo it. There is a limit to work that can be done safely, and some rest is required to avoid exhaustion and danger of freezing.

6. Perspiration is dangerous because it predisposes to frostbite and freezing. Keep clothes dry internally and externally. Change and dry socks and inner soles at least daily (twice daily if on trail). Underdress rather than overdress.

7. Clothing must be kept clean and free of oils or grease. Tie-ties on parkas, mukluks, etc., are put there to keep out snow and cold air, but they *must not* be tied so tight as to diminish circulation.

8. Do not wear shoe-mukluk or shoe-overshoe combinations. Under survival conditions you will lose a leg.

9. Shoes and socks in particular must not be tight. If you wear size 9s but 10s feel so good you always buy 11s, your Antarctic footwear should be size 12s and 13s to allow motion of the toes and to give sufficient insulation. Do not wear too many socks unless they are each successively larger in width as well as in length. (Socks which are too big give folds which cause pressure points and increased tendency to cold injury.) If your feet hurt, you are not hurt. When they STOP hurting, INVESTIGATE IMMEDIATELY, rewarm and exercise feet until sensation returns, change to dry socks and dry inner soles or grass if necessary.

10. Do not touch cold metal with moist, bare hands. If you should inadvertently stick a hand to cold metal, urinate on the metal to warm it and save some inches of skin. If you stick both hands, you'd better have a friend along.

11. Be careful in handling gasoline, kerosene or liquids other than water, for contact at cold temperatures will induce immediate frostbite.

12. Protective glasses or goggles must be worn at ALL times during daylight hours outdoors, whether the sun is shining or it is overcast. On sunny days, in addition, the nose and cheeks may be lampblacked to prevent glare. Scratchy, teary, light-sensitive eyes indicate snow blindness but there are no symptoms until the eyes have already been damaged.

Snow blindness results in a loss of two to five days at best—at worst, snow-blind people hold up their trailmates with their helplessness, fall in crevasses, or become lost and freeze to death.

13. Hot drinks add actual warmth to survival food, and they help maintain water requirements. Cook survival rations with plenty of water. This makes them more palatable and far more digestible. Boiled foods are more digestible than fried foods, and the juice gives you vitamins, minerals and needed water. Don't boil any food longer than necessary, for this destroys vitamins.

14. Whether you eat regularly or not, be sure you take in AT LEAST one to two quarts of water per day and no more than one-third of this as coffee (which is dehydrating). The vast majority of common ailments are prevented and treated by forcing fluids. Eating snow excessively cools the mouth and teeth. MELT it and drink.

15. Avoid alcohol except in small quantities—a toddy at bedtime, an occasional cup of cheer, O.K.—but drunkenness in the cold can mean death.

16. DON'T breathe too deeply the exhilarating polar atmosphere, particularly at temperatures lower than -25°F, without a face mask of some sort.

17. Remember sea and shelf ice can break up in a matter of minutes, due to ocean swells. Given a little wind or current, you will go to sea on your own private ice raft. Stay away from tidal cracks and ice edges. Give icebergs, headlands and glacial fronts a wide berth. They are ALL dangerous. NEVER camp on sea ice if it can be avoided.

18. Seals emerge to sun on the sea ice through breather holes more easily made and kept open in the thin ice near working cracks in sea ice, through tidal cracks along shore, near grounded bergs and at junctions of shelf and sea ice. Where seals are numerous and safe, man is not.

19. If you find yourself in the water KEEP IN MOTION. You can swim 100 to 200 yards *fully* clothed if you have to—in fact, your clothing helps rather than hinders buoyancy, so KEEP IT ON. If you get out on the ice and there is no help, KEEP ON YOUR FEET and KEEP IN MOTION some more. It is the *only* way you can keep warm until help arrives.

20. It has long been believed that undirected walk in the north is in a circle to the right —in the south, one is supposed to circle to the left from some fabled Coriolis effect in the inner ear! Actually solitary man probably circles in the direction of his shorter leg at either end of the earth. A compass, chart and previous study of terrain will help prevent circling. There is much more comfort in a survival manual read *before* an accident than afterward.

21. Never be careless with equipment, tools or clothing between use, for it can blow away or drift over in a matter of minutes. Stand up everything you can stick in the snow. If it won't stand up and you expect to find this object or location at a later date, it MUST be adequately flagged.

22. On the trail split essential items such as food, fuel, stoves, shelter, sleeping bags, survival gear and essential medical items between sled, trucks and individual packs, so that loss of one vehicle or man will not endanger the entire group. In small parties with only one radio or one survival essential, carry those treasures on the last sled.

23. Practice fire, man overboard, first aid and other drills until they are automatic and FAST. The life you save may be your own.

24. Keep comfortably cool, PHYSICALLY and MENTALLY, yet remain alert. Relax once and the artificial wall of security which you have painstakingly erected about yourself can give way without warning. There is never an uneventful journey in polar regions.

25. The life you risk is not only your own. It is also the lives of a lot of other people who will volunteer or be expected to go look for you if you come a cropper.

Require Doctor

Use Drop Message

Require Mechanical Help or Parts

Our Receiver Operating

Can Proceed, or Wait

Pick Us Up Aircraft Abandoned

Land Here, Pointing Direction

Don't Land Here

Yes, Affirmative

No, Negative

All Well

BODY SIGNALS may be used by polar survivors when a plane has noted their distress and is flying low. The plane answers "O.K." by rocking its wings or by flashing a green light, "not understood" by circling right or flashing a red light.

Bibliography

Ecology, Plants and Animals

Allen, Arthur A., *The Book of Bird Life* (2nd ed.). D. Van Nostrand, 1961.

Drimmer, Frederick, *Animal Kingdom*. Doubleday, 1954.

Hansen, Henry P., ed., *Arctic Biology*. Oregon State College, Corvallis, 1957.

Kimble, G. H. T., and Dorothy Good, eds., *Geography of the Northlands*. John Wiley & Sons, 1955.

Murphy, Robert Cushman, *Oceanic Birds of South America* (Vols. I and II). Macmillan, 1936.

Polunin, Nicholas, *Circumpolar Arctic Flora*. Oxford University Press, 1959.

Porsild, A. E., *Illustrated Flora of the Canadian Arctic Archipelago*. National Museum of Canada, 1957.

† Prévost, Jean, *Écologie de Manchot empereur*. Hermann, Paris, 1961.

Scheffer, Victor B., *Seals, Sea Lions and Walruses*. Stanford University Press, 1958.

Stefansson, Vilhjalmur, *The Friendly Arctic*. Macmillan, 1943.

Wild Animals of North America. National Geographic Society, Washington, 1960.

Wing, Leonard W., *Natural History of Birds*. The Ronald Press, 1956.

Peoples

Birket-Smith, Kaj, *The Eskimos*. E. P. Dutton, 1935.

Bosi, Roberto, *The Lapps*. Frederick A. Praeger, 1960.

Collinder, Björn, *The Lapps*. Princeton University Press, 1949.

Freuchen, Peter, *Book of the Eskimos*. World Publishing, 1961.

† Fried, Morton H., ed., *Readings in Anthropology* (Vol. I). Thomas Y. Crowell, 1959.

* Greene, John C., *The Death of Adam*. Iowa State University Press, 1959.

Jochelson, Waldemar, *Peoples of Asiatic Russia*. American Museum of Natural History, 1928.

Kroeber, Alfred Louis, *Anthropology* (rev. ed.). Harcourt, Brace, 1948.

Mowat, Farley, *People of the Deer*. Little, Brown, 1952.

† *Peoples of the Northwest Territories*. Issued under the authority of the Honourable Douglas S. Harkness, Minister of Northern Affairs and National Resources, Ottawa, 1957.

Spencer, Robert F., *The North Alaskan Eskimo*. U.S. Government Printing Office, 1959.

Wilkinson, Doug, *Land of the Long Day*. Henry Holt, 1956.

Arctic Exploration

* Anderson, Commander William R., and Clay Blair Jr., *Nautilus 90 North*. World Publishing, 1959.

Calvert, Commander James, *Surface at the Pole*. McGraw-Hill, 1960.

Caswell, John Edward, *Arctic Frontiers*. University of Oklahoma Press, 1956.

De Long, Emma, ed., *The Voyage of the Jeannette*. Houghton Mifflin, 1884.

Freuchen, Peter, and Finn Salomonsen, *The Arctic Year*. G. P. Putnam's Sons, 1958.

Harrington, Richard, *The Face of the Arctic*. Abelard-Schuman, 1952.

Hayes, J. Gordon, *The Conquest of the North Pole*. Macmillan, 1934.

MacMillan, Donald B., *How Peary Reached the Pole*. Houghton Mifflin, 1934.

Mirsky, Jeannette, *To the Arctic*. Alfred A. Knopf, 1948.

Mountevans, Admiral Lord, *Arctic Solitudes*. Philosophical Library, 1953.

Nansen, Fridtjof, *In Northern Mists*. W. Heinemann, London, 1911.

Peary, Robert Edwin, *The North Pole*. Frederick A. Stokes, 1910.

Shipton, Eric, *The North Pole*. Frederick Muller, London, 1957.

Weems, John Edward, *Race for the Pole*. Henry Holt, 1960.

Antarctic Exploration

Amundsen, Roald, *The South Pole* (Vols. I and II). Lee Keedick, 1913.

Byrd, Richard E., *Exploring With Byrd*. G.P. Putnam's Sons, 1937.

Hayes, J. Gordon, *The Conquest of the South Pole*. Macmillan, 1933.

Kearns, William H. J., and Beverley Britton, *The Silent Continent*. Harpers, 1955.

* Lansing, Alfred, *Endurance: Shackleton's Incredible Voyage*. McGraw-Hill, 1959.

Mills, Hugh R., *The Siege of the South Pole*. Alston Rivers, London, 1905.

Owen, Russell, *The Antarctic Ocean*. Whittlesey House, London, 1941.

* Scott, Robert Falcon, *Scott's Last Expedition*. John Murray, London, 1923.

Shackleton, Sir Ernest, *South*. Macmillan, 1920.

General Exploration

Debenham, Frank, *Discovery and Exploration*. Doubleday, 1960.

Heyerdahl, Thor, Søren Richter and Hj. Riiser-Larsen, *Great Norwegian Expeditions*. Dreyres Forlag, Oslo.

Kirwan, L. P., *A History of Polar Explorations*. W. W. Norton, 1960.

Leithäuser, Joachim, *Worlds Beyond the Horizon*. Alfred A. Knopf, 1955.

Mitchell, J. Leslie, *Earth Conquerors*. Simon & Schuster, 1934.

Polar International Geophysical Year

Antarctica in the International Geophysical Year. Geophysical Monograph No. 1. American Geophysical Union, 1956.

Barber, Noël, *The White Desert*. Thomas Y. Crowell, 1958.

Schulthess, Emil, *Antarctica*. Simon & Schuster, 1960.

Siple, Paul, *90° South*. G. P. Putnam's Sons, 1959.

Sullivan, Walter, *Assault on the Unknown*. McGraw-Hill, 1961.

Wilson, J. Tuzo, *IGY: The Year of the New Moons*. Alfred A. Knopf, 1961.

General

Cooper, Paul Fenimore, *Island of the Lost*. G. P. Putnam's Sons, 1961.

Debenham, Frank, *Antarctica*. Macmillan, 1961.

Fenton, Carroll Lane, and Mildred Adams Fenton, *The Fossil Book*. Doubleday, 1958.

Flint, Richard Foster, *Glacial and Pleistocene Geology*. John Wiley & Sons, 1957.

† Hedblom, Captain E. E., *Polar Manual*. Dept. of Cold Weather Medicine, U.S. Naval Medical School, National Naval Medical Center, Bethesda, Maryland, 1961.

Simpson, Frank A., ed., *The Antarctic Today*. A. H. & A. W. Reed, Wellington, New Zealand, 1952.

Steel in the Soviet Union. American Iron & Steel Institute, 1959.

Stefansson, Vilhjalmur, *Arctic Manual*. Macmillan, 1944.

Soviet Handbook 1959-1965: Statistics & Data Relating to the Soviet Seven-Year Plan (Soviet Booklet No. 57). Soviet Booklets, 1959.

* Also available in paperback edition.

† Only available in paperback edition.

Index

Numerals in italics indicate a photograph or painting of the subject mentioned.

Picture Credits

Credits for pictures from left to right are separated by commas, top to bottom by dashes.

Cover: Emil Schulthess from Black Star. 8: Paul Popper, Ltd. 10: Matt Greene. 11: Adolph E. Brotman. 12, 13: Kenneth S. Fagg. 17: Harry Groom from Rapho-Guillumette. 18, 19: Evelyn Stefansson—Emil Schulthess from Black Star. 20, 21: Emil Schulthess and E. Spühler from Black Star courtesy Conzett and Huber. 22, 23: Dr. Victor P. Hessler. 24, 25: Emil Schulthess from Black Star. 26, 27: S. D. MacDonald-National Museum of Canada, Fritz Goro. 28: Emil Schulthess from Black Star. 29: David Linton. 30: Wide World. 32 through 39: Douglas Gorsline. 41: Robert Edwin Peary courtesy National Geographic Magazine © National Geographic Society. 42, 43: Robert Edwin Peary courtesy National Geographic Magazine © National Geographic Society except top right Photo No. 306-NT-158614C in the National Archives. 44, 45: Robert Edwin Peary courtesy National Geographic Magazine © National Geographic Society except right Monkmeyer Press Photos. 46: Robert Edwin Peary courtesy National Geographic Magazine © National Geographic Society from Tim Gidal. 47: Monkmeyer Press Photos. 48, 49: Monkmeyer Press Photos, Robert Edwin Peary courtesy National Geographic Magazine © National Geographic Society. 50: United Press International. 52 through 57: Douglas Gorsline. 59: © Bjørn Finstad, Oslo courtesy Olav Bjaaland. 60: Paul Popper, Ltd. from Photo Researchers, Inc.—Paul Popper, Ltd. 61: Paul Popper, Ltd. from Photo Researchers, Inc.—Paul Popper, Ltd. 62, 63: left The Bettmann Archive; right Scott Polar Research Institute, Cambridge—© Paul Popper, London. 64: © Royal Geographical Society. 65: Culver Pictures—© Royal Geographical Society. 66, 67: © Royal Geographical Society. 68: top Charles Petersen. 69, 70, 71: Fritz Goro. 72: Emil Schulthess from Black Star. 75 through 79: Kenneth Gosner. 80, 81, 82: Frances W. Zweifel. 83: Niall Rankin. 84, 85: Jean Prevost of Expeditions Polaires Françaises, Emil Schulthess from Black Star—Mario Marret from the film *Aptenodytes-Forsteri.* 86: top Jean Prevost of Expeditions Polaires Françaises; center Mario Marret from the film *Aptenodytes-Forsteri.* 87: Jean Prevost of Expeditions Polaires Françaises. 88, 89: Expeditions Polaires Françaises,

Official U.S. Navy Photo by Walter M. Cox. 90, 91: Niall Rankin. 92 through 95: Michel Angot. 96 through 99: Fritz Goro. 100, 101: Ted Grant from National Film Board of Canada, Dr. Ian A. McLaren—Fisheries Research Board of Canada. 102, 103: John Molholm. 104: Tom McHugh from National Audubon Society. 107 through 111: Frances W. Zweifel. 113: Fritz Goro. 114, 115: John P. Kelsall—Canadian Wildlife Service, H. V. Vuori—Dalton Muir, Dr. Arturo E. Corte—U.S. Army Cold Regions Research and Engineering Laboratory, Dalton Muir from National Film Board of Canada (2). 116: Fritz Goro. 117: Otto Hegg from Jacobsen-McGill Arctic Research Expedition—Fritz Goro. 118, 119: Fritz Goro. 120: Albert Maag from Jacobsen-McGill Arctic Research Expedition. 121: John J. Koranda—Dalton Muir. 122, 123: Canadian Wildlife Service—left Dalton Muir; right C. J. Ott from National Audubon Society—Canadian Wildlife Service. 124, 125: S. D. MacDonald—National Museum of Canada, John Molholm—Doug Wilkinson. 126, 127: H.V. Vuori except bottom left C. J. Ott from National Audubon Society. 128: Fritz Goro. 130, 131: Matt Greene. 132: Mosesee of Port Harrison—Sywoolee of Port Harrison. 133: Sheeokjuk of Cape Dorset—Samuellee of Cape Dorset. 134, 135, 136: Mark A. Binn. 137 through 143: Doug Wilkinson. 144, 145: Pierre Marc, Mark Kauffman. 146, 147: Pierre Marc. 148: Sabine Weiss from Rapho-Guillumette. 149: Raoul Johnsson. 150: Ambrose Poulin, U.S. Army Cold Regions Research and Engineering Laboratory. 153: Matt Greene. 159: Associated Press. 160, 161: Bill Ray. 162, 163: Gordon Tenney. 164, 165: Fritz Goro. 166: George Silk—Official U.S. Air Force Photo. 167: R.C.A. Service Company. 168: Emil Schulthess from Black Star. 171: Mark A. Binn. 172, 173: Adolph E. Brotman. 175: Matt Greene. 177: Anthony Gow, U.S. Army Cold Regions Research and Engineering Laboratory. 178, 179: Russ Kinne from Photo Researchers, Inc. 180, 181: Emil Schulthess from Black Star. 182, 183: Emil Schulthess from Black Star—Fritz Goro. 184: Emil Schulthess from Black Star. 185: Fritz Goro. 186, 187: Jack Myers.

Acknowledgments

The editors of this book are particularly indebted to Carl R. Eklund, Chief, Polar Branch, U.S. Army Research Office; Eilif Dahl, Agricultural College of Norway; and William S. Osburn, Associate Director, Institute of Arctic and Alpine Research, University of Colorado. They read the entire book and criticized the chapters in their own areas of study. The editors are also indebted to Mrs. Evelyn Stefansson; Albert P. Crary, Chief Scientist, Office of Antarctic Programs, and George R. Toney, National Science Foundation; Erling Dorf, Professor of Geology, Princeton University; Henry Sharp, Chairman, Geology and Geography Department, Barnard College; N. L. Nicholson, Director, Geographical Branch, Canadian Department of Mines and Technical Surveys; V.E.F. Solman and John S. Tener, Canadian Wildlife Service; Michael Marsden and Colonel Walter A. Wood, Arctic Institute of North America; Fritz Muller, Jacobsen-McGill Arctic Research Expedition; Robert E. Frost and

W. R. Floyd, U.S. Army Cold Regions Research and Engineering Laboratory; A. L. Washburn, Department of Geology, Yale University; A. E. Porsild and A.W.F. Banfield, National Museum of Canada; William C. Steere, New York Botanical Garden; William O. Field, American Geographical Society; Mrs. Edward Stafford; John J. Teal Jr.; Paul Siple, Scientific Adviser, U.S. Army Research Office; Lady Suzanne Wilkins and Winston Ross for the estate of Sir Hubert Wilkins; the Canadian Department of Northern Affairs and National Resources; Wesley Johnson, Robert Berlin and Frank T. Richardson, Atomic Energy Commission; Joseph Dukert, Martin Marietta Company; Norman D. Newell, Curator of Fossil Invertebrates, and Malcolm C. McKenna, Assistant Curator, Invertebrate Paleontology, American Museum of Natural History; James Matthai, Geography Department, Teachers College, Columbia University; and Gordon Cartwright, U.S. Weather Bureau.

PRODUCTION STAFF FOR TIME INCORPORATED

Arthur R. Murphy (Vice President and Director of Production)
Robert E. Foy, James P. Menton and Caroline Ferri
Text photocomposed on Photon equipment under the direction of Albert J. Dunn and Arthur J. Dunn

Printed by R. R. Donnelley & Sons Company, Crawfordsville, Indiana,
and Livermore and Knight Co., Providence, Rhode Island
Paper by The Mead Corporation, Dayton, Ohio
Bound by R. R. Donnelley & Sons Company, Crawfordsville, Indiana